Thriving on Stress

SELF-DEVELOPMENT FOR MANAGERS
A major new series of workbooks for managers, edited by
Jane Cranwell-Ward at Henley Management College

This series presents a selection of books, in workbook format, on a range of key management issues and skills. The books are designed to provide practising managers with the basis for self-development across a wide range of industries and occupations.

Topics to be covered in the series include: stress management; assertiveness training; effective problem-solving; management of change; and team building. All the books in the series contain exercises and self-assessment material.

Each book will relate to other relevant books in the series, so that the series provides a coherent new approach to self-development for managers. Closely based on the latest management training initiatives, the books are designed to complement management development programmes, in-house company training, and management qualification programmes such as CMS, DMS, MBA and professional qualification programmes.

Jane Cranwell-Ward is the Director of Company Programmes at Henley Management College. She has extensive experience running management training programmes and stress management workshops, in both public and private sectors. She is the author of *Managing Stress*, published in 1986 by Pan.

Thriving on Stress

Jane Cranwell-Ward

 London

First published in 1987 by
Pan Books Ltd

Published 1990
by Routledge
11 New Fetter Lane, London EC4P 4EE

Reprinted 1993

Printed and bound in Great Britain by
Biddles Ltd, Guildford and King's Lynn

British Library Cataloguing in Publication Data
Cranwell-Ward, Jane
   Thriving on Stress – 2nd ed.
   1. Personnel. Stress. Management aspects
   I. Title II. Cranwell-Ward, Jane. Managing Stress
   658.382

ISBN 0–415–04465–0

Contents

— *Preface*

The self-development series for managers has been created to meet a growing need to help practising managers, working in a range of industries and occupations, to acquire skills and capabilities to meet the challenges they face in the 1990s.

In my professional life, as Director of Company Programmes at Henley Management College, I am required to help develop senior and middle managers through the attendance of development programmes. The self-development series has been written to compliment this type of activity and educational course. Alternatively the books can be used very successfully by managers as part of a self-managed development programme.

The 1990s will be a challenging decade, and many organizations are facing turbulent times as they change to meet competition in the UK and Europe. To help meet these challenges managers must operate at peak performance and learn to thrive on stress.

Many books have already been written on the subject of stress. Some are written from an organizational perspective and give extensive narrative on the symptoms and causes of stress. The management of stress is treated in a rather detached way. Other books are written by medical experts and concentrate on stress-related illness and ways of achieving a healthy life. Few seem to adopt the self-help approach needed to develop the skills of thriving on stress.

My interest in the subject originally developed from training and lecturing to large numbers of practising managers and personnel practitioners. I also have a personal interest in the subject, having experienced and suffered from excessive stress in the past. This led me to write my first book, entitled *Managing Stress.*

In preparation for my first book I interviewed and administered questionnaires to 200 managers to learn how they experienced stress and coped with it. Case material will be included throughout this book. Names have been changed to protect those who gave their time so willingly. Thank you to all those who completed questionnaires and were interviewed. The material I collected proved extremely useful.

More recently I have developed my interest and understanding of the subject, running many stress management workshops for a wide range of employees and sectors of employment. *Thriving on Stress* is the outcome of this further work. I should like to thank colleagues, friends and workshop participants in all the organizations I have worked, especially the Borough of Barking and Dagenham, Henley Management College, Kingston Polytechnic, Royal Borough of Kingston and South West Thames Regional Health Authority.

Particular thanks goes to Stephanie Gale-Burkitt for her help and support whilst I was writing the book. I am grateful to my colleagues in Company Programmes. Working with them provided the stimulation needed to develop the second book. Finally I would like to thank Dave Francis for his creative ideas and constructive critiques. His contribution has greatly enhanced the quality of the book.

I now feel more able to thrive on stress successfully and hope others will benefit from some of the experience I have developed over the years. *Thriving on Stress* includes some of the original diagnostic work which has proved to be so helpful to people seeking to manage their stress levels. The book reflects my more recent thinking that stress can be viewed positively and channelled to achieve enhanced performance levels.

Jane Cranwell-Ward

— *Introduction*

Thriving on Stress has been written to help you, the practising manager. The book should enable you to cope with stress more effectively and to avoid the consequences of excessive stress. If you are suffering from stress, want to learn why you are, and how you can thrive on it, then this is the book for you.

Firstly I will define what I mean by the term 'manager'. I define a manager as a person who has control over resources, including other people. I intend to use the term in its broadest sense to include, for example, engineers acting as team leaders, ward sisters managing other nurses, and senior accountants co-ordinating the work of more junior staff.

In writing this book I am very aware that many people suffer from stress, including those at more junior levels. You may discover that this applies to your subordinates. The book will help you to develop strategies for coping with their stress. They also will benefit from reading the book. Whilst I have written *Thriving on Stress* for the manager, much of the material has proved useful and relevant to people in non-managerial positions. The symptoms of stress are likely to be identical whether you are employed as a manager, teacher or dentist. Strategies for thriving on it will also be equally appropriate.

Stress is difficult to define, so it must be perfectly clear how I intend to use the term. For this reason, the next chapter of this book will deal exclusively with understanding stress, including the physiological background to it, and will provide the conceptual framework for the rest of the book. The view I will be taking is that stress results when a person's perceived capacity is insufficient to meet the demands of the situation. In other words, stress is the result of imbalance.

Most people view stress as a negative feature in their lives. This may be true, but in learning to manage stress effectively you may come to believe that the experiences of stressful periods can actually be beneficial to you. If channelled in the right way, stress can be used to provide the energy for increased performance and self-development. The title of this book *Thriving on Stress*, has been chosen to highlight this.

The assessment you make of a situation is partly dependant on your personality disposition, self-esteem and self-confidence. You may thrive on a lot of excitement in your life, or you may prefer a fairly calm situation. You need to have good self-insight to optimize a situation.

Developing resistance to stress is an important aspect of stress management. Managers are becoming much more health-conscious as they realize that being healthy makes them more resistant to the impact of stressful situations. Many drink less at lunch-time, count calories and take more exercise; some have become actively involved in sport. You will be given the opportunity to assess your vulnerability to stress – a necessary part of thriving on stress – and you may need to make adjustments to your total lifestyle if necessary.

Organizations are also developing a growing awareness of the importance of stress and its impact on employees. More are referring employees for health and fitness tests. Others are running stress management courses or providing stress counselling for staff. Large organizations are also beginning to provide sports facilities, such as gymnasiums and swimming pools, to help employees get fit and maintain fitness levels.

Managing has become very demanding. You, as a manager, may have to achieve targets with fewer staff and tighter financial resources. In addition, organizations are undergoing rapid technological change; this results in feelings of uncertainty and insecurity amongst the employees. To cope with change your staff may need to be re-trained, re-deployed or even made redundant.

Of course stress is not only with you at work. It permeates every aspect of your life and may emanate from situations arising outside work. For example, one in four marriages is likely to end in divorce. This is ranked as one of the highest causes of excessive stress. Once excessive stress levels develop they remain with you at work and at home. This book will focus on sources of stress and coping mechanisms applicable to both situations.

Effective managers are becoming aware of the increased pressure they are experiencing and are learning to recognize the symptoms. How do you react? Do you sometimes find yourself feeling unable to cope, feeling as if you are living on a knife edge, don't know which way to turn and are unable to think straight? You are not alone; many managers have reported similar feelings. You are obviously aware of your reactions. Others are less able to recognize the signs, or are less prepared to admit that they are suffering from the effects of excessive stress.

Few managers can afford to ignore the effects of stress. More working days are lost through stress-related illness than ever before. It now has greater impact than days lost through strikes. Medical experts have clearly demonstrated that stress is a killer; there is a high correlation between excessive stress and coronary heart disease. Many other illnesses are stress related also.

The impact of stress is not restricted to illness. It also has a detrimental effect on important functions of management such as the effectiveness of decision-making, the quality of interpersonal relationships, the standard of work, the quality of working life and of course, ultimately, the level of productivity. You will be encouraged to recognize your own indicators of excessive stress so that you can take the appropriate action quickly, thus preventing a build-up of harmful effects.

Once you realize you are experiencing excessive stress, you need to adopt a strategy for managing it. I do not advocate one strategy as being the panacea for all ills; I believe that a range of strategies exist. To thrive on stress you need to manage your physical, emotional, mental and spiritual well-being.

Thriving on Stress has been written in the form of a workbook. I hope you will develop a deeper understanding of stress, and an awareness of yourself and your reactions to stress through diagnosis and reflection. You will then be in a position to thrive on stress by establishing and maintaining the right balance in your life.

To help you achieve this I have divided the process into steps. You will be invited to participate in a series of exercises designed to measure your vulnerability to stress, sources of stress, your preferred stress levels and reactions you experience when stress levels become excessive. At this stage you might find that you are not suffering from excessive stress. If this is the case then give the book to a highly stressed friend who might benefit from reading all of it! Alternatively, keep it for the time when you, your spouse or one of your subordinates suffers from stress.

Once you have diagnosed your stress you will be able to complete the process of thriving on it. You will be able to assess the effectiveness of your current coping strategy, to assess alternative methods of optimizing your stress level, and learn to make adjustments if necessary.

I believe that to acquire the skill of thriving on stress requires commitment and involvement on behalf of the reader. You don't necessarily need to read the book from cover to cover but try to resist the temptation of skimming past the exercises, intending to complete them tomorrow. Regrettably 'tomorrow' never seems to come.

The first stage of stress management requires you to participate in the exercises to increase self-awareness. You will also need to spend time reflecting on your life, particularly stressful periods. The more fully you understand yourself, and your reactions to stress, the more successfully you will be able to manage excessive stress in your life.

The second stage of stress management requires a commitment to make changes, if necessary, particularly in cases where pressure is excessively high or excessively low. Effective managers are those who maintain the right balance in their lives. The philosophy of balance advocated by the Japanese, for example, when they practice Tai-Chi each day has much to commend it. Those who work excessively hard in their early life are likely to burn themselves out by their mid-forties. On the other hand, most effective managers cannot operate without pressure. They are likely to become apathetic and bored, and achieve sub-standard performance levels.

A few years ago stress management was viewed as something only the inadequate few needed to do. Today, professional athletes, tennis players and musicians have all learned the value of managing stress levels to achieve peak performance. Follow the steps outlined in *Thriving on Stress* and you, too, could become a more effective manager.

— What is stress?

Before embarking on the workbook phase you need to understand the nature of stress and learn to view it as a positive force. You should know what happens to your body and mind when exposed to a threatening situation or to excessive pressure, and be aware of the interactive nature of stress.

THE MANAGER'S VIEW OF STRESS

Stress means different things to different people. In the survey managers were asked 'What do you mean by the term stress?' How would you answer this question? Pause for a moment and decide what response you would make. The most common replies included:

- too much work and too little time to do it;
- a feeling of anxiety;
- being unable to cope;
- too much pressure;
- feeling tired and irritable;
- emotional pressure.

Two interesting points emerge. First, there are two types of answer – those related to the cause of stress, and those related to the effects of stress. In future, *causes* of stress or stressors will be differentiated from the *effects* of stress or the reactions to stress. Second, most people seem to have a negative view of stress. This does not have to be the case. Pressure can be seen as positive, providing you with extra energy to meet external or self-imposed demands. Some managers described stress as a feeling of elation and of being able to rise to a challenge. You can probably think of a situation in your own life when you surprised yourself at the performance you achieved. This will be discussed more fully later in the book.

Having given a brief explanation of stress the managers interviewed gave a much more detailed description of what stress meant to them. Two of these described below help to demonstrate the different ways managers can experience stress.

Joe was a quiet, meticulous person working as an electronics engineer in a large high-technology establishment. He felt able to keep on top of the technical aspects of his job – he knew what he was doing and felt in control. A year before he had been promoted to the position of team leader of an important project. Faced with the task of managing a group of junior engineers he felt inadequate, and described the situation as stressful. Questioned further, he explained that he found delegation difficult and was unused to motivating others. He also experienced pressure from the problem of relating to his team. As time progressed he felt tense and regularly suffered from headaches. Joe saw stress as having a damaging effect on work performance.

Joe's response to stress was negative. He assessed himself as inadequate to cope with the situation facing him and tension built up inside him. Eventually he suffered from headaches and his work performance deteriorated.

Duncan viewed stress rather differently. He was employed as a marketing manager for a large pharmaceutical company. His job required him to travel, meet a wide range of people and make presentations to large groups. He was an outgoing person, found his job challenging, and thrived on pressure.

He associated stress with making a presentation to a large group of people. If you have ever been asked to do this you can probably remember the sensation as you stood up in front of the audience. Duncan described it as a rush of energy firing his body, making his heart beat faster, and focusing his mind sharply. This reaction helped him to give a lively and dynamic performance.

These case histories illustrate the different perceptions people have of stress. Some people thrive on stress, others experience distress. One secret of stress management is to adopt a positive attitude to stress (as Duncan has). The extra energy, generated as a result of imbalance, can then be channelled to achieve enhanced performance. Negative outcomes can thus be avoided, provided the period of excessive pressure is not too long.

A study of expert research on stress shows that it can be described in one of three ways – the stimulus approach, the response approach, or the interactional approach.

The stimulus approach

Those who adopt this approach describe stress as an external factor or force. The *Oxford Dictionary* definition of 'stress' is 'pressure', thus adopting a stimulus view. Engineers also use this meaning of the word when they calculate the stress a building must withstand. Their view is that a building has to be able to cope with certain stresses – the load or demand placed upon it. The response to stress is strain. If the building is subjected to excessive stress permanent damage will result. This is shown in Figure 1.

Figure 1 The stimulus approach to stress

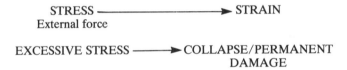

STRESS ———————————➤ STRAIN
External force

EXCESSIVE STRESS ———➤ COLLAPSE/PERMANENT
DAMAGE

People are also able to withstand certain pressures, but their level of resistance varies. Some cope with excessive pressure in their lives, whilst others collapse very quickly. Some researchers have developed this approach further, stating that stress arises when the level of demand on the person departs from optimum conditions.

External factors will be referred to as stressors. You must become aware of the stressors in your life in order to manage stress successfully; you will be given the opportunity to do this in a later step.

The response approach

People who adopt a response-based approach focus on the reactions made by the person to environmental demands. The response may be physiological, for example your heart beats faster, or psychological, for example you feel irritable. This is shown in Figure 2.

Figure 2 The response approach

STRESSORS ⟶ STRESS
(in the environment)

Physiological
Reaction

Psychological
Reaction

The response approach was adopted by Dr Hans Selyle, an Austrian-born physician. He experimented with animals and found that whatever demands were placed on the animal, such as extremes of temperature or a threatening situation, the reaction was the same. He called this reaction the general adaptation syndrome, and believed an identical syndrome was also experienced by people.

This approach provides a useful starting point for understanding stress, but probably oversimplifies its complex nature. Today, researchers believe that responses may vary from situation to situation. This has led to a third view of stress, the interactional approach.

The interactional approach

This approach takes the understanding of stress a stage further, by intensively studying the interaction between the person and his or her environment. Up to now people have been viewed as taking a fairly passive role, reacting fairly automatically to the situations in which they find themselves.

More recently, researchers have realized that people play a more interactive part, weighing up the demands of the situation in which they find themselves and appraising their own capability to meet those demands. This approach describes stress as the result of an imbalance between the level of demand placed on people, as they perceive it, and their perceived capability to meet the demands.. This is shown in Figure 3 and is more easily understood by considering an example.

Figure 3 The interactional approach

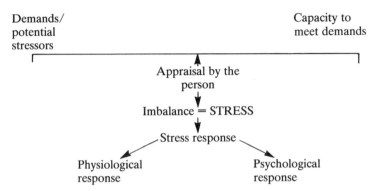

Most of you probably need to get work done using secretaries. The next case was described by a manager, and is a good illustration of the components of stress. Margaret, Jill and Fiona were three secretaries, each of whom experienced stress for different reasons. Margaret was a very capable secretary who seemed to thrive on pressure. She provided secretarial support for several managers and she always seemed to be on top of her work. Then two new managers joined the department and Margaret was expected to provide secretarial support for them. Up until that time Margaret experienced a balance between demands and her capacity to meet those demands. The extra demands placed upon Margaret were such that she suddenly felt unable to cope, her work output fell dramatically and she failed to meet deadlines. She was suffering from stress, and her work performance deteriorated as a result.

Stress may also be a result of a lack of capability. Jill became stressed for this reason. She was a lively girl, and had been promoted to personal secretary, more on the grounds of personality than for her secretarial skills. She had difficulty establishing priorities and was unhappy when left to work on her own initiative. Whenever her manager gave her work without clear guidance she suffered from stress. Unlike Margaret, she perceived herself as inadequate, rather than experiencing excessive demands.

Stress can also result from a lack of stamina to meet the demands of work. Fiona suffered from this problem. She, like Margaret, was very capable, and normally managed to meet the demands of the job. Unfortunately she regularly caught colds, and this caused her to experience stress. In this case her physical resources were inadequate to meet the demands of the situation.

These three examples highlight the individual nature of stress. Everyone perceives situations differently. Even the same person can perceive the same situation differently on separate occasions. The interactional approach provides the most comprehensive view of stress and has useful implications for stress management. Accordingly, this is the approach used throughout this book.

A DEFINITION OF STRESS

Stress is the physiological and psychological reaction which occurs when people perceive an imbalance between the level of demand placed upon them, and their capability to meet those demands. To be able to thrive on this imbalance you need an understanding of the physiological reaction which takes place.

THE PHYSIOLOGICAL REACTION TO STRESS

When you react to a threatening situation, several changes take place in your body. You are probably familiar with the feelings you experience when you narrowly miss having a car accident, are about to sit an examination or become exposed to a frightening situation. The way you feel is the result of a number of physiological changes taking place in your body. These changes are shown as a flow diagram in Figure 4. The sequence progresses as follows:

1   When you are faced with a threatening situation, chemical messages in the brain are carried along tracks, called neurons, to the hypothalamus. This is situated in the lower part of the brain. It is very sensitive to the effects of drugs, stress and intense emotion and is largely responsible for changes in appetite, weight, water balance and mood.

2   The hypothalamus produces a chemical called corticotrophin (CRF). This chemical, along with others, passes to the pituitary gland, situated at the base of the brain.

3   The pituitary gland plays an important part in reactions to stress, by controlling the flow of hormones from other glands.

Figure 4 The chemistry of stress

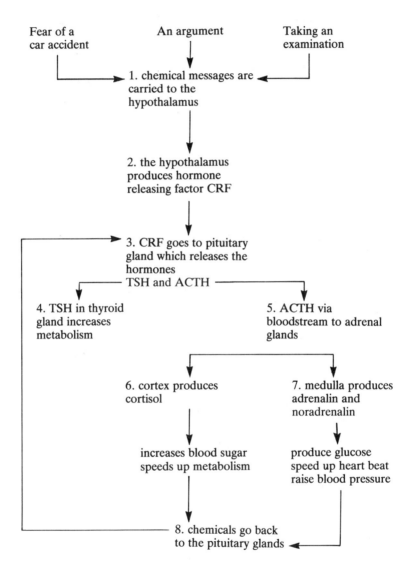

It produces the adrenocorticotropic hormones (ACTH and TSH).

4   TSH travels to the thyroid gland at the front of the neck. This controls energy levels, increased energy resulting from an increase in metabolic rate.

5   ACTH travels to the outer layer, or cortex, of the adrenal glands. The adrenal glands are two small glands lying close to the kidneys.

6   The chemical cortisol is produced in the cortex. This increases the level of sugar in the blood and speeds up the metabolism of the body.

7   ACTH also travels to the middle, or medulla, of the adrenal glands. In the medulla chemical reactions take place, and the hormones adrenalin and noradrenalin are produced. These are secreted into the bloodstream, which produces a response sometimes referred to as 'the fight or flight response'. This response will be discussed more fully below.

8   Chemicals are then fed back from the medulla and cortex of the adrenal glands to the pituitary gland. This continues to control the stress response.

The effect of the chemicals and hormones on your body helps to explain why you experience particular symptoms when you suffer from stress. These can act as warning signs and early diagnosis is important to avoid harmful effects building up. The reactions will be discussed fully in Step Five (page 58).

Ian, a civil engineer, gave a nice illustration of the stress response when he described the start of a typical day. He woke up with the alarm ringing and remembered he needed to be at work early that day. He jumped out of bed, showered, shaved, swallowed a quick cup of tea, and ran out to the car. Within minutes he was stuck in rush-hour traffic. Would he make his first appointment, he asked himself. Already Ian could feel the pressure mounting. He arrived at work with only seconds to spare. The doors closed as he reached the lift but Ian decided to wait, rather than walk up the five flights of stairs. He entered his office and immediately his boss arrived and started to criticize the report he submitted a week before. Ian felt the urge to strike him. Instead he sat down at his desk. His boss left and Ian looked at the pile of papers in his in-tray. He sat reflecting on the boss's comments and felt his neck muscles tighten and his stomach churn.

You can probably understand what has been happening to Ian. The chemical changes necessary to make Ian get out of bed have built up more and more as the morning has progressed. Without much physical activity, the detrimental effects are able to build up. Ian would have felt much better if he had walked up the stairs, rather than wait for the lift. This would have reduced his level of tension. Note the urge to be aggressive when Ian's boss criticized him. Instead Ian kept his feelings to himself, and experienced a tension in his neck and in the stomach. He may have reduced the tension if he had confronted his boss, or even hit him!

The 'fight or flight' response is one in which adrenalin and noradrenalin makes the body 'rev. up' for action, rather like an aeroplane before take-off. This is one of the most primitive responses and was obviously essential to the caveman's survival. It gave them the energy they needed to cope with dangerous animals, it was their survival mechanism. Today you seldom need to be physically active, and the hormones sometimes accumulate in your body, leaving you feeling frustrated, irritable and impatient.

Adrenalin and noradrenalin also have other effects. In particular they influence how alert you feel. Adrenalin seems to focus concentration and helps to improve memory. Too low a level of noradrenalin causes depression. Exercise such as swimming, running or dancing raises the level of noradrenalin and helps to lift depression.

THE RELATIONSHIP BETWEEN STRESS AND PERFORMANCE

Everyone needs a certain level of pressure to perform well as, it provides the stimulation necessary to achieve creativity and innovation. Without sufficient pressure your performance will be restricted. In certain circumstances stress can enhance performance. When you feel you have insufficient resources to meet a situation the stress reaction is triggered and creates the extra energy needed for demanding situations. In this case, stress is the spice of life, helping you to innovate, explore unknown territory and rise to new challenges. Positive stress enhances performance and helps you flow with the pressure, just like a windsurfer.

Stress can also be destructive and negative. Faced with insufficient resources the stress reaction is again triggered but when you feel anxious and tense, your energy is sapped, your perspective on life becomes distorted and you struggle to cope. In this case performance drops off dramatically and you feel exhausted – stress has become distress. The relationship between stress and performance is illustrated in Figure 5.

Figure 5 The relationship between stress and performance

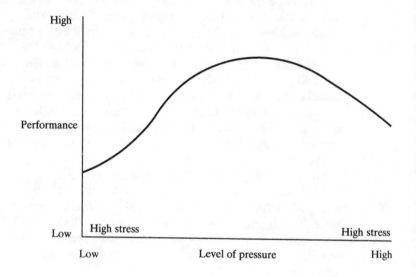

Figure 5 shows that a lack of pressure is as stressful as excessive pressure. The secret of thriving on stress is to keep a careful balance between stress and relaxation. If this balance is maintained it stops the onset of exhaustion, and keeps the performance curve rising. How is this balance maintained?

The balance between stress and relaxation

When you are under pressure the sympathetic part of your nervous system becomes active. You become aware of your heart beating faster, your breathing becomes more intense and your blood pressure increases. As pressure decreases the parasympathetic system becomes activated, which demobilizes the body. Thus breathing becomes slower, the heartbeat lowers and blood pressure drops. This enables your body to recover from the active period. If you become over-stressed your parasympathetic system ceases to become active. Your body continues to be highly active and you become exhausted.

To be able to thrive on stress, your sympathetic and parasympathetic nervous systems need to operate in a see-saw fashion. Periods of activity must be interspersed with inactivity and relaxation. Strategies to thrive on stress will help you to maintain this balance.

To review this section, compare the features of positive stress with those associated with negative stress.

Positive stress – thriving on stress
Faced with pressure your energy level rises to meet the challenge. You feel alert and in control of the situation. You are able to take life as it comes, dealing with issues and problems without becoming over-anxious. When the pressure is over you are able to relax. You enjoy life and are able to laugh, enabling tension to flow from your body. You feel self-confident and have a high level of self-esteem.

Negative stress – experiencing distress
Faced with pressure you may at first feel very wound-up and active. You feel tense and out of control of the situation. Every incident becomes a problem; life seems to revolve around a series of crises and you feel very anxious. Over a period of time you may become exhausted and feel despondent or apathetic. You feel constantly uptight and unable to relax. You have difficulty enjoying life and seldom laugh.

This workbook will help you to identify the type of stress you experience and develop strategies to ensure you, and others around you, thrive on stress. You are now ready to proceed to the first part and complete the diagnostic phase.

How to use the book

There is no one right way to thrive on stress. Instead, there is a wide range of possible options, some of which will be suitable for you. This belief has been a major influence on the way the book has evolved. It is written in the form of a workbook. This means that you are required to take an active part, first by completing exercises to diagnose factors relevant to stress, and second by completing exercises to help you create your own self-development programme.

You do not need to read the book from cover to cover immediately, unless you feel the problem is so urgent! A better alternative is to work through the book more slowly, allowing time for reflection and discussion with colleagues, your spouse, or friends. This will help you to develop a broader perspective on yourself and the way you currently manage stress.

You may decide to work through the book with others. After workshops on stress management people often tell me they have discussed the exercises with colleagues and friends. The strategies which evolve from shared reflection seem to be far more successful than those when the task is tackled individually.

To be able to make full use of this book you need a clear idea of its structure.

It is divided into four separate sections. In Part I you will work through a series of exercises designed to help you diagnose factors relevant to thriving on stress. In Part II you will review and consolidate your findings from Part I and consider the implications for thriving on stress. In Part III you will consider various strategies for thriving on stress and plan your own personal strategy. In Part IV you will review how to help others thrive on stress and develop a plan of action.

Within these four sections there are eleven steps which you complete in sequence.

PART I: DIAGNOSIS

Step one: Disposition and stress

The stance you take in a situation is partly dependent on your disposition. You may thrive on a lot of excitement in your life, or you may prefer a much calmer situation. You need to have good self-insight to identify your own balance. This first step will give you the necessary insight.

Step Two: Assessing vulnerability to stress

Developing resistance to stress is important. Managers are becoming much more health-conscious. This should help them to become more resistant to stressful situations. In the workbook you will be able to assess vulnerability to stress. To thrive on stress you may need to make certain changes to your total lifestyle.

Step Three: Exploring the sources of your stress

As managers you probably face a range of stressful situations at work and at home. This step will focus on sources of stress applicable to both situations and will help you to clarify issues which generate stress in you.

Step Four: Assessing the level of change in your life

Organizations are undergoing rapid change. This results in feelings of uncertainty and insecurity. This step will enable you to calculate the amount of change, good and bad, which you have experienced recently, as a measure of the demands placed upon you.

Step Five: Reactions to stress

Effective managers need to be aware of increasing stress and recognize the way they react. Do you sometimes feel unwell, and unable to cope, or is stress the spice of life for you? This step will help you to identify whether your reactions are positive, negative or both. You will be encouraged to recognize negative reactions in order to take appropriate action quickly, preventing the build-up of negative effects.

PART II: REVIEW AND CONSOLIDATION

Step Six: Review, consolidation and developing a vision of the future

This step follows logically from Part I. You need to spend time bringing the data together, and reflecting on it. In particular you need to assess your current stress level. When you have a clear view of your current situation you will then be able to spend time developing your vision of the future. This will help you to select the most appropriate strategy for thriving on stress.

PART III: STRATEGIES AND TECHNIQUES FOR THRIVING ON STRESS

Step Seven: Assessing your current strategies

This first step in Part III will help you to assess your current methods for managing stress. You will complete an exercise which will help you to differentiate the unsuccessful from the successful strategies and techniques you are using at the moment.

Step Eight: Optimizing performance

This step will help you to identify the extent to which you flow with the pressure, thrive on stress, and therefore maximize performance. Two factors influence the way you respond to stress in a given situation – your level of competence, and the level of challenge. Your responses are also influenced by your level of self-confidence, commitment and control over the situation. This step will help you to identify your responses and will help you to develop ways of working to maximize performance.

Step Nine: Strategies to thrive on stress

There are a wide range of strategies available to enable you to thrive on stress. Your choice will be influenced by the diagnostic work done in earlier steps and by your values and disposition. This step will discuss the available strategies, and will help you to choose the one most appropriate for you. Once you have chosen a strategy you will then be able to study it before moving on to the next step.

Step Ten: Your stress management strategy

This step will encourage you to identify what needs to be done to implement the strategy you have selected. This is obviously an important step. It will ensure you take action, and are able to evaluate the outcome.

PART IV: HELPING OTHERS TO THRIVE ON STRESS

Step Eleven: Helping others to thrive on stress

This final step recognizes the importance of managers taking responsibility for those around them, helping them to thrive on stress. You will be able, as a result of working through this step, to develop a plan to help prevent excessive stress occurring in the first place. You will also develop a plan to help others to optimize their performance, and to cope more effectively with excessive stress.

The steps follow a logical sequence, and should be completed in order as shown in Figure 6.

Finally, a word of explanation. The inventories in this book have been designed as self-help activities, not scientifically validated questionnaires. For this reason you should use them as guides to help you to reflect, and come up with your own assessments, rather than viewing the results as precise measurements.

This book should not be viewed in isolation. There are additional books in the self-development series which you may find help you to thrive on stress. I hope that reading this book will stimulate your interest and encourage you to read other books. This one book cannot attempt to cover all the skills associated with thriving on stress in sufficient depth. (Other books in the series include *Effective Problem Solving, Managing Change* and *Developing Assertiveness.*)

Now is the time to start on the first step. I hope you enjoy using the workbook, and your future life thriving on stress.

Figure 6 Managing stress

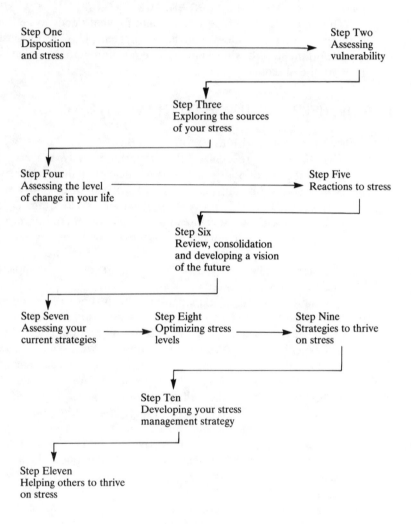

Part I
Diagnosis

Step One
Disposition and stress

An important first step towards thriving on stress is to identify your disposition. Once you have completed this step you will be able to establish your appropriate stress level, and your vulnerability to suffering from the negative effects of stress.

The stance you take in a situation is influenced by your disposition. This is defined as your usual temperament or frame of mind. Placed under excessive pressure you may remain calm or become very tense. Your disposition will influence your preferred stress level – for instance, if you are a very active person you may thrive on a high level of pressure; whereas if you are a person who worries you will prefer a much lower stress level. Disposition will also affect vulnerability, or the likelihood of suffering from the negative effects of excessive stress. If you are very ambitious you run the risk of pushing yourself too hard, unlike a more relaxed person who is far less vulnerable.

A straightforward analysis of disposition has been developed by American researchers. They identified two types of manager whom they designated Type A and Type B. They described the Type A manager as ambitious, competitive and time-driven, and far more likely to suffer a heart attack than a Type B colleague. They described the Type B manager as relaxed, unambitious and casual about time.

To understand fully the relationship between disposition and likely reactions to excessive stress, a more elaborate approach is needed. I have developed a basic typology which includes six recognizable types:

- the Ambitious type
- the Calm type
- the Conscientious type
- the Nonassertive type
- the Lively type
- the Anxious type

In Step One I will define and describe the types, and refer to likely stressors, vulnerability to stress and preferred stress levels. When you have read the descriptions you will be required to identify the type which bears the closest resemblance to yourself. Please note that the descriptions have been written in the third person. I have used the pronoun 'he', rather than he/she, to avoid the descriptions becoming clumsy. The descriptions apply equally to both men and women.

TYPE 1: THE AMBITIOUS TYPE

Definition A person having a strong desire for success or achievement.

Description

The Ambitious type closely resembles the Type A manager. He is likely to be successful in his chosen career, and driven by the need to succeed. His commitment to his career is likely to be high and he is likely to be active and energetic, seldom finding time to relax. He is not prepared to waste time, and may become rather impatient if required to wait for anything or anyone. Inevitably Ambitious types are very common in management positions, a job which usually requires an ambitious, energetic person.

When relating to other people this type may tend to be aggressive and argumentative. He has a strong need to dominate others, possibly because of hidden insecurities. Personal relationships and home life take second place in his life. He may even cancel a family holiday if necessary, if work commitments are pressing.

Internal pressures and demands are likely to be high. The Ambitious type tends to set high standards and drives himself to achieve them. He finds failure hard to accept. Overload and meeting tight self-imposed deadlines are potential stressors for the

Ambitious type. Possible signs of stress include sleeplessness, high blood pressure, heavy smoking or drinking and heart problems.

Preferred stress level High.
Vulnerability to stress High.

TYPE 2: THE CALM TYPE

Definition A Calm type is tranquil and placid, and does not easily become disturbed, agitated or excited.

Description

The Calm type closely resembles the Type B manager. He is likely to be patient and unworried, and unlikely to set too many impossible objectives for himself. He probably allows himself time to think over and reflect on past achievements, unlike the ambitious type who is always striving to achieve goals. However, he is likely to achieve less than his more ambitious colleague. He may have the capacity to appreciate people's good characteristics and is less likely to be become obsessed by the inadequacies of others. This approach enhances his self-esteem.

In relationships with others, the Calm type is usually able to give and receive affection and praise. He need not play a dominant role and is seldom irritated by others. He probably keeps a balance between work and home. He is more able to devote time to leisure pursuits. Inner tensions are likely to remain low. Other people, or stress carriers, are potential stressors.

Preferred stress level Moderate to low.
Vulnerability to stress Low.

TYPE 3: THE CONSCIENTIOUS TYPE

Definition A Conscientious type is a person who is meticulous, taking great care over everything required of him.

Description

He is likely to be very reliable and single-minded, but may be stubborn. In his desire to achieve the task thoroughly, he can become obsessive. The Conscientious type may become over-concerned with getting things right, paying too much attention to detail, thus losing sight of longer term objectives.

Wanting to get the job done properly he probably prefers a set routine, and is less able to manage change than the calm or ambitious type. He may feel thrown when something unexpected happens. He is less likely to seek challenge in his life, preferring the security associated with working within his range of competence.

As a manager, the Conscientious type is likely to believe in authority and tradition. This will influence the way he interacts with superiors and subordinates, giving a high degree of respect to his superiors, but expecting the same treatment by his subordinates. Home life is likely to be equally organized, and he may like to follow routines quite rigidly. There may be a degree of inner tension and turmoil, particularly if the Conscientious type feels he is losing control.

Potential stressors include other people, particularly those who fail to plan ahead. An excessive workload can also cause the Conscientious type stress.

Preferred stress level Low to moderate.
Vulnerability to stress Moderate, high at times of change.

TYPE 4: THE NONASSERTIVE TYPE

Definition A Nonassertive type is unable to assert himself, and has difficulty standing up for his own rights.

Description

The main concern of the Nonassertive type is to please others, thus avoiding conflict. In his fear of how others may react he runs away from situations rather than confronting them. To avoid conflict, he may interact with others in such a way that people either misunderstand him or ignore his requests; instead, they may take advantage of him.

The Nonassertive type may have difficulty in saying 'no' to requests of help from others. Relationships with others are likely to be problematic. This stems from his inability to express his own needs, his desire to please others and his fear of confrontation.

The Nonassertive type may experience inner tensions. These

develop from feelings of resentment that others are taking advantage of him. He may also experience frustration from his inability to satisfy his own needs in his desire to accommodate the needs of others. These inner tensions are likely to be a major source of stress for the Nonassertive type. He may also find the demands from others, and his inability to assert his own identity, stressful.

Preferred stress level Moderately low.
Vulnerability to stress Moderate.

TYPE 5: THE LIVELY TYPE

Definition A Lively type is a person who is full of vigour and experiences mental and emotional intensity.

Description

The Lively type is likely to live life to the full. Unlike the Ambitious type, who is driven by achievement, the Lively type needs a varied and interesting life. His basic philosophy is that 'variety is the spice of life'.

The Lively type thrives on change and may become bored with the same job for too long. He probably needs a high level of stimulation and challenge, and thrives on the surge of energy which results from the flow of adrenalin through his body. In his desire for excitement and challenge, he may take unnecessary risks, act impulsively and put himself under excessive pressure.

The Lively type is likely to enjoy relating to other people. However, because of his need for a varied life he may not stay in one place for long.

Inner tensions may develop if the Lively type pushes himself too far. He may run the risk of burn-out. Sources of stress for the Lively type are likely to be routine work, lack of change, and internal pressures.

Preferred stress level High.
Vulnerability to stress Low; high if he exerts excessive pressure on himself.

TYPE 6: THE ANXIOUS TYPE

Definition An Anxious type is a person who is worried and tense because of possible misfortune.

Description

The Anxious type worries a lot and finds it difficult to relax. He is obsessed with doing things right. He plans for every eventuality, but will inevitably fail. His normal reaction is to panic, which is exacerbated when things go wrong.

The Anxious type devotes a great deal of mental energy to focusing on the future. However, his thoughts are unconstructive because a lot of time is spent worrying about what might happen, rather than attending to what is actually happening. Typical of the Anxious type is over-concern with other people's evaluations and judgement. Self-confidence and self-esteem are likely to be low. This interferes with relationships at work and at home. Changing environments create considerable uncertainty and evoke defensive reactions rather than rising to the challenge.

The Anxious type is likely to experience a high degree of internal pressure and turmoil, and will probably have fairly intense negative emotions, including feelings of self-doubt. Life generally is likely to be stressful for the Anxious type, but challenging work, change and uncertainty will probably be particularly stressful.

Signs that the Anxious type is suffering from stress include the possibility of persistent headaches, an inability to think straight, a predisposition to become dependant on tranquilizers and a vulnerability to nervous exhaustion.

Preferred stress level Low.
Vulnerability to stress High.

Now that you have read the descriptions of the six types, complete the following exercise to help you identify the type which fits your disposition most closely, and assess the implications for your preferred stress level and vulnerability to stress.

EXERCISE: IDENTIFYING YOUR DISPOSITION

OBJECTIVE To identify your disposition and assess implications for your preferred stress level and vulnerability to stress.

PROCEDURE 1 Rank the types in order of their resemblance to your disposition. You may need to re-read the description to complete this task.

1 Lively

2 Ambitious

3 Non assertive

4 Anxious

5 Calm

6 Conscientious

2 Study the three types most like you and write down the preferred stress levels for each type.

1 High

2 High

3 Low

Is there any difference in preferred stress levels for the three types? If there is a difference you will need to take account of this when you develop your personal strategy for thriving on stress.

3 Study the three types most like you and write down the vulnerability for each type.

1 Low/High if stressed

2 High

3 Moderate

Do any of the types make you vulnerable to suffering from the negative effects of stress?

When you have completed this exercise, move on to Step Two.

Step Two
Assessing vulnerability to stress

If you are vulnerable you are open to attack, and likely to be wounded by excessive stress. The likelihood depends on several factors. Your resistance to stress is enhanced by your physical and emotional well-being, and, at a deeper level, by developing understanding and acceptance of yourself. Attention to these factors will give you the fitness, energy and self-confidence necessary to thrive on stress. Step Two will help you to assess the extent to which you will be able to respond positively to stress.

Compare your own body with a car. You are probably very careful to use the correct grade of fuel. Do you pay as close attention to the food you eat? If dirt gets into the carburettor you immediately become aware of the effect. You need to become as sensitive to your own body and its limitations. How much alcohol can you safely drink without feeling ill the following day, and which foods disagree with you? You also know the capacity of your car and its maximum speed. You would never keep pushing the engine beyond its limits, but you may abuse your body, forcing it to keep going when it may need to be given time to recover and to restore energy. You probably have your car serviced regularly, but do you give yourself the same care and attention?

To be able to thrive on stress you need to increase your resistance, making yourself less vulnerable to the effects of negative stress. What makes you more or less vulnerable to stress? There are several factors which influence physical and psychological well-being, and these factors are interactive. Psychological factors, for example emotional problems, can have an effect on your physical state of health, and will lower your resistance to stress-related illness. They will be discussed more fully later.

First you need to assess your vulnerability to excessive stress by completing a short exercise.

EXERCISE: HOW VULNERABLE AM I TO STRESS?

OBJECTIVE To help you assess some of the factors which may make you more or less resistant to stress. The exercise is subjective, but managers completing this exercise found that it helped them to reflect on their lives, and the extent to which they took care of their physical and psychological well-being.

PROCEDURE Study each of the following questions and give each one a score of 3, 1 or 0. *A score of 3* means you can say definitely yes/always to the statement, e.g. 'I spend time walking each day.' Full agreement with this statement would give a score of 3. *A score of 1* means you are uncertain about your response or you are in between, e.g. 'I avoid drinking at lunchtimes.' If you occasionally drink at lunchtime, you would give this statement a score of 1. *A score of 0* means you can say definitely no/never to the statement, e.g. if you never play sport you would give statement 35 a score of 0. Some items, of necessity, are negative statements, e.g. I never work at weekends. If you never work at weekends you would agree with the statement and give it a score of 3.

1 I eat the right food in the right quantities. ☐ 1

2 I avoid drinking alcohol at lunchtimes. ☐ 3

3 I exercise to the point of perspiration at least three times a week. ☐ 0

4 I have a network of friends and acquaintances. ☐ 0

5 I am contented with my sex life. ☐ 1

6 I have at least one hobby/interest I pursue regularly. ☐ 1

7 I never work at weekends. ☐ 3

8 I engage regularly in prayer or meditation. ☐ 0

9 I limit my intake of coffee, tea and coca-cola to five cups a day.   `3` 3

10 I enjoy a drink of alcohol rather than needing a drink, or I do not drink alcohol.   `3` 3

11 I exert moderate physical energy in my daily life.   `3` 3

12 I give and receive affection regularly.   `1` 3

13 I regularly achieve sexual satisfaction.   `1` 1

14 I allow myself time to relax every day.   `1` 3

15 I restrict myself to realistic workloads and never work to excess.   `0` 1

16 I usually find solutions to my problems.   `3` 3

17 I maintain the appropriate weight for my height.   `3` 3

18 I never drink alcohol alone.   `3` 3

19 I climb the stairs rather than use the lift.   `0` 3

20 I am able to display emotions rather than allow negative feelings to build up inside me.   `0` 1

21 I am seldom impotent/frigid.   `3` 3

22 I get seven to eight hours' sleep at least four nights a week.   `1` 1

23 I never let work dominate my life.   `0` 1

24 I believe in myself.   `1` 1

25 I avoid adding too much salt to my food.   `3` 3

26 I rarely have a drink of alcohol when I return home from work.   `0` 1

27 I follow a regular programme of exercises.   `1` 1

28 I have people who are close to me and with whom I can discuss intimate problems.   `1` 1

29 I have a loving sexual relationship.   `3` 3

30 I do something for fun at least once a week.   `1` 3

31 I avoid talking about work in social situations.   `1` 1

32. I have an inner feeling of tranquility. [0] 1

33 I eat regular meals each day and avoid frequent snacks. [1] 1

34 I would describe myself as a moderate drinker of alcohol (an average of 0–2 drinks a day) or I do not drink alcohol at all. [3] 3

35 I participate in a sport each week. [1] 1

36 I have colleagues at work who give me emotional support. [0] 1

37 I enjoy a stable emotional relationship. [3] 3

38 I am able to enjoy myself. [1] 1

39 I never work in the evenings. [0] 1

40 I feel I have a deep sense of belonging, of being a part of things. [1] 1

41 I drink water/mineral water regularly. [0] 0

42 I smoke fewer than five cigarettes a day, or I do not smoke at all. [3] 3

43 I spend time walking each day. [3] 3

44 I would seek help from friends or obtain professional advice if necessary. [0] 1

45 I seldom feel sexually frustrated. [3] 3

46 I am able to spend time doing nothing. [3] 3

47 My home life and work is equally important to me. [1] 1

48 I have learned to rise above stressful situations. [0] 1

When you have completed the exercise transfer the score for each question into the appropriate space in the table below, next to the question number, and total up the scores for each category.

Vulnerability profile

A	B	C	D	E	F	G	H
1 [7]	2 [3]	3 [6]/	4 [o]	5 [\]	6 [1]	7 [1]3	8 [o]
9 [3]	10 [3]	11 [3]	12 [1]3	13 [1]	14 [1]>	15 [o]1	16 [3]
17 [3]	18 [3]	19 [o]3	20 [0]1	21 [3]	22 [1]	23 [0]\	24 [1]
25 [3]	26 [o]1	27 [1]	28 [1]	29 [3]	30 [1]3	31 [1]	32 [o]\
33 [1]	34 [3]	35 [1]	36 [o]1	37 [3]	38 [1]	39 [o]1	40 [1]
41 [o]	42 [3]	43 [3]	44 [6]1	45 [3]	46 [3]	47 [1]	48 [o]\

Totals

A	B	C	D	E	F	G	H
[11]	[15]16	[8]12	[2]7	[4]	[8]12	[3]8	[5]7

Interpreting the scores

    A Healthy diet
    B Avoiding alcohol and cigarettes
    (C) Programme of exercise
    (D) Emotional well-being
    E Fulfilling sex life
    (F) Relaxation and enjoyment
    (G) Balance between home and work
    (H) Self-understanding and acceptance

The eight factors were selected as those which health experts and psychologists commonly agree influence vulnerability to stress.

What do the scores mean?

You are able to score a maximum of 18 and a minimum of 0 for any one factor.

A score of 15 or more: first ask, 'have I been really honest when I answered the questions?' Some managers admitted that their scores reflected the situation they would like to exist, rather than reality. If your scores are genuine then that particular factor is unlikely to make you vulnerable. If you score 15 or more for all the factors then you are more likely to be able to thrive on stress than the person with much lower scores.

A score of 9 or less: you are more likely to experience stress negatively. If you obtained any low scores look back over the questions and establish the reasons. The next part describes the factors associated with vulnerability. When you have read this next part you may decide to make certain changes to your life.

Factors affecting vulnerability

A review of this section will help you to reflect on the need for life changes. Step Nine will help to consolidate the changes into a plan of action.

A: Healthy diet

Nutrition is a subject in its own right. This section will merely help you to assess whether your diet is adequate. Eating a well-balanced diet helps your body to operate efficiently and provide you with the energy needed to maintain a good state of health and to thrive on stress.

You need a balance of fresh food including protein, particularly white meat and fish, a small amount of fat, limited carbohydrate and plenty of fresh fruit and vegetables. Nutrition experts also recommend a high level of fibre in your diet. Restrict sugar intake, and avoid red meat and excessive salt.

Vitamin tablets may also help you, particularly when you are under severe pressure. Vitamins B and C are useful on these occasions. Vitamin B affects mental attitude and helps you to cope with stress. Vitamin C helps you to resist the harmful effects of stress.

Action If you are concerned about the quality of your diet, it may help to read a book on the subject. Review your diet and assess whether you need to make any changes.

B: Avoiding alcohol and cigarettes

A small amount of alcohol probably enhances your well-being, and helps you to relax. Drunk to excess it becomes very damaging to your health and impairs work performance. Excessive drinking, particularly spirits, increases the risk of suffering from cirrhosis of the liver. You are less likely to make effective decisions or achieve clarity of thought, and your judgement may become impaired. The executive is greatly at risk from drinking excessively.

An occasional cigarette can help you to relax and to concentrate. Cigarettes do, however, quickly become addictive. The more you smoke, the greater the health risk. There is a known correlation between smoking and lung cancer, cardiovascular disease and bronchitis. Like drinking, there is a tendency to smoke more when you feel stressed.

If you are a smoker, become aware of what this does to you. Cigarettes contain three active ingredients – nicotine, tar and carbon monoxide. When you inhale, nicotine is taken into the lungs and stimulates both the respiratory tract and also the brain. Nicotine also has negative effects. It narrows the coronary arteries and raises blood pressure and cholesterol levels. Tar builds-up in the lungs, resulting in bronchitis and lung cancer.

Action If you had a low score, review your drinking and smoking habits. Is this a factor which requires changes to be made?

C: Programme of exercise

A planned programme of exercise helps to dissipate the harmful effects of stress, by burning up excessive adrenalin and preventing the build-up of cholesterol in the arteries. Exercise helps to build up stamina and reduce the tensions of everyday life. It also helps combat fatigue and lift depression.

Action If you have a low score, consider adopting a strategy in Step Nine which will help to develop your physical stamina.

D: Emotional well-being

This factor can be subdivided into three components which will be considered separately:

- emotional support
- ability to display emotions
- opportunity to give and receive affection

Emotional support If you have people with whom you can discuss intimate problems, the situation is less likely to develop out of all proportion in your mind. Whilst a self-reliant, independent approach to life is desirable and necessary for managers, there are times when you may find you need support from others. You may receive this support from your spouse, relatives, friends or colleagues.

Action Review your support network and decide whether or not it is adequate. Assess whether you are able to take full advantage of this support network. Several of the managers interviewed experienced difficulty talking to others about personal problems.

Ability to display emotions Most people experience emotional reactions to situations at work and at home, but vary in their capacity to display these emotions. If someone annoys you at work do you let them know you are annoyed or do you bottle it up inside? The ability to display emotions helps you to develop a more positive approach to life. If you allow negative feelings to build up, you become frustrated or depressed. Display positive feelings and people are likely to reciprocate these positive feelings, enhancing your sense of well-being.

Action Spend time reflecting, and decide whether you are able to display feelings in the appropriate way. There will be a strategy in Step Nine to help those who need to manage their emotions more effectively.

Opportunity to give and receive affection People's physical well-being is enhanced by the opportunity to give affection. For example, medical evidence has shown that some patients recovering from open-heart surgery recover more quickly if they have a pet they can stroke. You may be aware that people vary in the amount of affection they need to give and receive. If you were deprived of affection as a child you may need less affection as an adult, or spend the rest of your life trying to make up the deficit.

Action Insufficient opportunity to give and receive affection will create tension in your life. Think of the opportunities available to you; is the balance satisfactory, or do you need to make any changes to your life?

E: Fulfilling sex life
This is a highly effective and enjoyable way to release tension and make you more able to withstand stress. The sexual act alone

enhances physical well-being. The benefits are much greater when sex is part of a deep emotional relationship. In this situation, possibly as many as four of the factors under discussion are satisfied.

Action At this stage you need to ask yourself whether your sex life is sufficiently satisfying. Are you falling into the trap of allowing work to dominate? If you become over-stressed, a symptom is a loss of interest in sex. Does this apply to you? Perhaps changes in your life are necessary.

F: Relaxation and enjoyment

You need balance in your life: for the successful manager this means a hobby or interest which provides the opportunity to unwind. The manager who no longer finds his job demanding may need to find stimulation outside work. This may be found by becoming involved in local government, or through undertaking voluntary work.

Without the opportunity to switch off from work, the likelihood that you will suffer from stress becomes much greater. The key question you must ask yourself is, 'Do I have fun in my life?' You also need to assess whether you allow yourself time for complete rest and relaxation. Are there times during the week when you do very little? Do you ensure that you have enough sleep at night? Rest is essential to remain in a good state of health. Many managers live their lives on a knife-edge, close to burn-out and collapse.

One of the best forms of relaxation is a holiday. This provides everyone with the chance to get away from the everyday routine at work and at home. You do need to plan the holiday carefully, matching the choice with your ability to unwind. You also need to allow time for readjustment when you return to work. Several of the managers interviewed failed to take their full holiday allowance. They had reached a stage of feeling indispensable, and had lost sight of the benefits of a holiday.

Action Think back over the last few years and consider whether you have allowed yourself sufficient time for relaxation and rest. If not, you may be operating close to exhaustion, and you are most unlikely to be performing at peak efficiency. Techniques to help relaxation have been included in Step Nine.

G: Balance between home and work

Many of you may feel the balance between home and work is inappropriate. In the Victorian age a favourite saying was 'the devil finds work for idle hands'. The saying still holds true in the minds of many managers. Those of you who are engaged in interesting, rewarding work can probably work extended hours, with a high level of commitment, without personal sacrifice – you are able to thrive on work and able to work hard and play hard, thus maintaining the appropriate balance in your life. Some of you may find your work excessively hard, leaving no time for relaxation.

Those of you who perhaps find your work frustrating, boring or unsuccessful may fall into the trap of becoming obsessed with work. Unfortunately, if this happens to you, the harder you work the more inefficient you become and you find yourself working even harder to compensate for the inefficiency.

Action Take a cold, hard look at yourself – are you in danger of becoming a workaholic? Are you always working, or thinking about work, even when you are at home?

H: Self-understanding and acceptance

If you understand yourself, your needs and motives, and accept your limitations, you are more likely to achieve a feeling of inner peace. This enables you to accept the stress you experience and keep situations in perspective.

There are a number of techniques which you can practise which will help you to achieve a feeling of inner peace – these include meditation, relaxation and self-healing. They are particularly helpful to reduce the impact of stress, by slowing the body down and reversing the stress reaction. People who regularly practise relaxation and meditation report a number of beneficial effects. It can, for example, help to lower your blood pressure. Most people say their self-esteem is increased, and they feel calmer and more able to withstand the effects of stress. They also feel that it broadens their perspective on life, and they feel more in control of their destinies.

Action Do you strive for a deeper feeling of peace and tranquility? If this is the case, you may like to consider one of the techniques mentioned. These will be discussed further in Step Nine.

Now that you have had a chance to assess your vulnerability to stress, reflect on the factors associated with vulnerability, by completing the following review.

EXERCISE: VULNERABILITY REVIEW

For each of the vulnerability factors, summarize how well you are observing the factor.

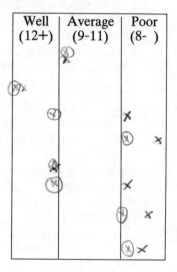

	Well (12+)	Average (9-11)	Poor (8-)
A Healthy diet			
B Avoiding alcohol and cigarettes			
C Programme of exercise			
D Emotional well-being			
E Fulfilling sex life			
F Relaxation and enjoyment			
G Balance between home and work			
H Understanding and acceptance of self			

As a result of this review I need to take the following action:

When you have completed the review move on to the next step.

Step Three
Exploring the sources of
your stress

Ask a group of people what causes them stress and the list is likely to be wide-ranging. Having talked with large numbers of people over the last four years I have formed the view that the sources of stress can be grouped into several key areas. Life events, which are positive or negative changes to your life, have been omitted from this step. They will be used in the next step to assess the level of change you are currently experiencing.

At some time in your life you are likely to experience excessive pressure. Some people perpetually operate in a state of 'overload'. Others are affected only under extreme circumstances.

Your reaction to excessive pressure may be positive or negative, depending on whether you view it as a challenge or a threat. Problems are likely to arise when you view a situation negatively. This step has therefore been designed to help you to identify the sources of your stress which result in a negative reaction. Once you have identified the source or sources you are then in a stronger position to take appropriate action.

You will remember that in the introduction stress was defined as the physiological and psychological reaction which occurs when people perceive an imbalance between the level of demand placed upon them and their capability to meet those demands. This step will help you to identify just what triggers the reaction.

EXERCISE: EXPLORING THE SOURCES OF YOUR STRESS

OBJECTIVE The purpose of this exercise is to enable you to identify the causes of your stress.

PROCEDURE Reflect back over the last five years and identify as many causes of stress you have experienced as you can. Write these down, together with the major stressors in your life now.

When you have completed this exercise go on to read the following list of ten generic stressors, and compare this list with your own. Each stressor will be defined below. They are not listed in order of importance.

1: SELF-IMPOSED PRESSURES

Self-imposed pressures are those which occur as a result of unrealistic self-expectations, a lack of self-confidence, fear of incompetence and a lack of self management.

Unrealistic expectations You may find you set unachievable targets for yourself and expect very high standards. Failure to achieve the targets, and the pressure to achieve very high standards, creates stress. People who operate in this way could be described as perfectionists. By having realistic expectations you are more likely to build your confidence and feel a sense of achievement.

Lack of self-confidence Fear is the main motivator for those who lack confidence. You may have doubts regarding your skills, attributes and knowledge to perform successfully in a range of situations. Develop your self-confidence by learning to assess the situation and deciding what has to be done. This switches you from a 'feelings' to an 'action' mode, a more positive approach.

Fear of incompetence More specifically you may doubt your ability to achieve a given task. This often occurs when you are promoted or move to a new job. Once more, assess the situation and decide what you need to do to achieve the task.

Lack of self-management If you suffer from excessive overload you should first ask yourself, 'How effective is my self-management?' Managers with demanding lives need to organize their workloads and take care of their own well-being by having adequate exercise and rest, and eating the right food.

Fiona, a ward sister, gave an amusing case taken from her early days in training. A staff nurse told her to give a patient a suppository, and asked Fiona if she knew how to give one. As Fiona said, 'I didn't want to look silly by saying I didn't know. I thought she had given me the clue when she told me to check the patient's breathing at the same time. I carefully inserted a suppository up each nostril, then noticed the patient looked rather blue in the face. I asked the nurse to check that everything was correct. Of course the suppositories were in quite the wrong part of the patient. The nurse said she wouldn't have minded, but I hadn't even taken their outer wrappings off!' This case makes an important point – that we need to avoid trying to cover up our internal fears.

2: UNFULFILLED NEEDS AND DESIRES

These are pressures which occur when important needs and desires remain unsatisfied, generating feelings of aggression, frustration or misery. Important needs include material rewards, recognition, security, status, power and achievement.

Various people have theorized about the needs which drive you. Needs provide you with a source of energy, and help to explain the way you behave in different situations. Some needs are more easily within your own control, whilst others remain elusive and can be a major source of stress. Affiliation needs and the need for meaningful work will be dealt with under the headings of unfulfilling relationships and lack of job satisfaction respectively.

Material rewards The high level of affluence in Western society has resulted in people attaching much greater importance to material possessions. Many feel that their status in society is measured on the basis of these possessions. As a result, people commit themselves to high mortgages and a level of spending which is difficult to sustain. People should perhaps remind themselves of the old adage, 'cut your coat according to your cloth.'

Recognition people like to receive acknowledgement for the contribution they have made. This may take the form of promotion, financial reward or a thank-you. When achievements pass unrecognized people can feel very demotivated. Regrettably, you may need to draw your achievements to the attention of others to ensure just recognition.

Security Some people like to be able to predict the future. They are low risk-takers who will feel pressurized at times of change when their future suddenly becomes uncertain. If security is an important need for you, then do everything in your power to ensure your life is stable and secure so that you can cope with the inevitable changes which you will have to face. This will be discussed more fully in the next step.

Status People who feel they need to be respected by others have a high need for status. They may satisfy this need through their rank or from the fringe benefits which go with a job, such as the size of company car, having a car phone or having a large office. You may need to satisfy this need in the community if you fail to satisfy it at work.

Autonomy People who have a high need for autonomy seek to be in control of the way their lives are structured, and set their daily objectives. In an organization, autonomy increases with seniority. The junior workforce are far less likely to satisfy autonomy needs than senior management. You need to identify the areas in your life where this need can be satisfied and learn to accept those areas which are beyond your control.

Edward was employed as a lecturer at a polytechnic. He had a high degree of commitment to his work and played a positive role in the activities of his department. He was very ambitious and was striving for promotion. Some opportunities became available, but he was unsuccessful. Failure to satisfy his need caused him considerable stress.

Many of you may identify with Edward. At each level in the organizational hierarchy, promotion becomes more restricted. Only a very small percentage of managers will become masters of industry, for instance. Others will have to come to terms with the situation. Those who fail to do so are far more likely to suffer from stress.

3: PROBLEMS OF DAILY LIFE

These are pressures which occur from situations usually beyond our immediate control, which by themselves may appear insignificant but cumulatively can contribute to levels of stress. They might include:

- commuting
- queuing
- losing items
- lateness (self and others)
- computers
- rail strikes
- machine breakdown (at home and at work)
- interruptions
- jet lag

In these situations you should remain calm, when possible, to ensure minimum impact. Techniques which lower stress levels, such as relaxation techniques, meditation and yoga, should be helpful. These will be discussed more fully in Step Nine.

4: EXCESSIVE DEMANDS

Excessive demands are pressures which occur as a result of too much to do and too little time to do it. The demands may come from your job or from non-work-related responsibilities. You may also feel overloaded because of the number of competing demands, which relate either just to work, or to a combination of home and work demands. Alternatively, the level of your work may be too demanding.

Your assessment of your workload is highly subjective and will vary. Sometimes you will feel able to undertake large amounts of work. At other times, smaller amounts become a burden. This is partly a reflection of mental attitude. Perhaps Blanchard has the solution; writing in *Leadership and the one-Minute Manager* he says, 'work smarter not harder.' You may suffer from overload because you are working ineffectively.

5: LACK OF JOB SATISFACTION

These stressors are the pressures which occurs when the job fails to meet the needs of the job-holder. Whilst this is likely to be a personal assessment, most managers are likely to want challenge, interest, autonomy and a vision of what is expected of them.

You spend a high proportion of your life at work. For this reason you need to be employed in a job which meets your needs and capabilities and provides you with the scope to fulfil your potential. At particular stages in your life you are likely to reappraise your career; some believe that this happens on a cyclical basis approximately every seven years. At times, changes may be necessary. This is particularly likely to happen between the ages of thirty-five and forty, and is referred to as the mid-life, or mid-career, crisis.

Mark had just passed through the career decision-making phase when I interviewed him. He had been employed as a teacher in a comprehensive school. 'As a teacher I was beginning to feel quite disillusioned and stressed by the education system. The final straw came when I was asked to paint the classroom. Could you imagine a doctor being asked to paint the surgery, or a ward sister to paint the ward? I realized the time had come to find a job which more closely matched my needs and capabilities.' He looked for a more suitable job in industry, seeking a career in personnel.

6: UNFULFILLING RELATIONSHIPS

Pressure occurs when relationships fail to fulfil expectations. At work, relationships should provide stimulation, challenge, support, and possibly friendship. Outside work, similar needs are likely to prevail but in addition there is a need for affection and closeness.

Relationships at work Most managers spend seventy-five per cent of their working day relating to others. This activity brings with it the possibility of personality clashes, lack of trust and support, criticism, competitiveness and lack of co-operation. This pressure is even greater for those who are introvert or experience more difficulty relating to people. In relationships with superiors, trust and support are the two most important characteristics. You need to feel that you are free to make your own decisions but have someone to refer to when necessary. In relationships with colleagues, co-operation is important, especially if you need to work closely together. In relationships with subordinates you need to give support and clear objectives, and meet the needs of your subordinates. Once you trust their competence you must be prepared to delegate work to them. In this way you are far more likely to build an effective team with good working relationships.

Relationships at home These relationships bring different types of pressure. Family and friends can make heavy demands on you or have unrealistic expectations of you. Most people have a basic need to relate to others. Pressure will develop when you feel misunderstood or rejected. The more intimate the relationship, the more vulnerable you will feel. When you experience difficulties with your partner the pressure can be intense, and you are unlikely to be able to leave this pressure behind when you go to work.

As you will remember from Step Two, the greater your support network and the more you feel fulfilled by your close relationships, the more resistant you will become to stress. You need to set aside the time and energy needed to build effective relationships outside work – we sometimes neglect the most important people in our lives.

7: FEAR OF THE FUTURE

Pressure can arise from feeling fearful about your future both at work and outside work. Those who feel fearful are likely to be uncertain, insecure and less able to take advantage of the opportunities open to them. At work there may be concerns about the long-term viability of the company, or more specifically whether the person concerned will still be employed. At home there may be fears about the future of a relationship, the welfare of ageing relatives or the upbringing of children. Most psychologists would agree that a preoccupation with the future is unhealthy. Whilst we are able to plan for certain contingencies in the future, we can only control the present.

8: CONCERN FOR LOVED ONES

Pressure can arise out of concern for the well-being of those who are close to us, including parents, spouse, our children, and friends. This stressor is related to life outside work, and to several 'key' people in our lives.

Parents/grandparents As they grow older, parents and grandparents may start to become less independent and their health may begin to deteriorate. Once one of the partners dies, problems can become more acute, and the pressure builds up.

Spouse/partner Concerns may be job-related or personal. We can often experience the stress of our partners, particularly where there is an empathetic relationship.

Children Concerns can relate to their development, or problems associated with growing up. There may be educational problems, and when children are studying for exams pressure is likely to build up in parents. There will also be pressure as children launch their own careers, get married and have their own families.

Friends Friends can experience all the problems outlined above, which can cause you concern.

In all these situations you need to ensure that you make available sufficient time to give the necessary support. You may find some of these situations could pass you by if you become too engrossed in your work.

9: IMBALANCE BETWEEN WORK AND HOME

Pressure occurs when there is an inappropriate balance between the time and energy spent at work compared with the time and energy given to home life.

Managers are particularly susceptible to the dangers of becoming totally absorbed by their work. Their departure time in the morning becomes earlier and earlier, they arrive home at night later than ever, carrying a very full brief case. They are very likely to fall asleep watching television.

Some managers have the problem of travelling. This may be confined to the UK, in which case they are more likely to be at home at weekends. Others who have to travel world-wide may lose their weekends, and may also return home jet lagged.

Unfortunately, just at the time when work demands are greatest, pressure at home can often be quite intense. Think back over your career; if you are in your late 20s or early 30s, your career has probably reached an important stage. At this phase in your life, you may also have a young family. This will be a greater or lesser strain depending on whether you are a man or a woman, and if you are a man whether your wife also works. Obviously the strains of the dual-career family are much greater.

The number of dual-career families, where both partners pursue a career and at the same time raise a family, has increased over the years. The man has to play a more active role in the home, and the woman has the task of fulfilling two roles. The woman's dual role of worker and wife/mother may cause her further stress if she feels she is neglecting her 'traditional' role as homemaker.

Reference was made in Step Two to the importance of an appropriate balance between home and work. Clearly, these two aspects of your life can often be in conflict, and it is not always easy to find the right balance. Some managers tell me that they cope with the problem by keeping their weekend totally free for the family. Others 'steal' some time each day to ensure the balance is maintained.

Richard was a management consultant. His work often took him away from home, sometimes several nights a week. 'I just don't have enough time to do all I want to do. My family need me when I return home, and I seem to have less and less time for myself.' He was divorced and took his family responsibilities seriously. At times he felt quite stressed, feeling a loyalty to his children's needs, but also an equally strong pull to pursue his career and be the breadwinner. Ultimately he cut back on some of his work commitments, to ensure a smoother home life.

10: ILL HEALTH

Pressures occur as a result of feeling unable to work at full capacity because of ill-health. When managers are ill their performance can easily deteriorate. The illness may be severe enough to necessitate time off work. This invariably happens during busy periods, adding to the pressure. The illness may be serious enough to cause anxiety and concern about recovery.

Research has shown that much illness is stress-related, setting up a vicious circle. If the illness is not too serious, you need to devote time and effort to regaining full health. This means ensuring that you have adequate relaxation, and enough sleep to give your body the chance to recover.

REVIEW

You have now had a chance to study the major sources of stress. As you will be aware, the generic categories are not mutually exclusive. The intention was to make them sufficiently wide-ranging to cover the majority of potential sources. To complete this step you now need to complete the following exercise, 'Exploring the source of your stress'. When this step is complete, move on to Step Four.

EXERCISE: EXPLORING THE SOURCES OF YOUR STRESS

OBJECTIVE To enable you to identify where your stress originates, what is the specific stressor, when it occurs, the degree of control you have over the situation, and finally, to decide whether each stressor is likely to increase or decrease over the next six months.

PROCEDURE 1 Rank the generic stressors in order of their importance to you. 2 Complete the chart below.

Generic stressor	Ranking
Self-imposed pressures	1
Unfulfilled wants and desires	10
Problems of everyday life	5
Excessive demands	2
Lack of job satisfaction	4
Unfulfilling relationships	6
Fear of the future	8
Concern for loved ones	9
Imbalance between home and work	3
Ill-health	7

Are there any other stressors in your life not covered by the ten generic stressors?

Select the three stressors currently most important to you and complete the chart below.

Stressor	*Describe the situation when and where it occurs*	*Level of control:* *High* *Medium* *Low*	*Will stress increase or decrease?*

Step Four
Assessing the level of change in your life

Stress is the outcome of a complex relationship between yourself and the environment in which you operate. Throughout life you are faced with a whole series of changes, sometimes beyond your control, which have to be managed. Sometimes you will feel stimulated by the changes in your life. At other times, especially when the changes are particularly unwelcome, stress levels can become excessive. Step Four will help you to assess both the level of change in your life, and its impact upon you. You need to repeat this step from time to time, to keep a check on your stress level.

Since writing *Managing Stress* I have become aware of the extent to which change has become a part of everyday life in companies. Whilst most managers would claim to thrive on a certain level of change, when the level becomes excessive, and the organization turbulent, even the most resistant of managers are likely to experience high stress levels.

Life events which cause stress have been extensively researched. A ranking of stressful events was drawn up by researchers in the USA, known as 'The Holmes and Rahe social readjustment rating scale'. The research was conducted across a range of cultures. Findings show a remarkable similarity in the degree of importance attached to specific life events by the different cultural groups. The most stressful event, requiring the greatest adjustment, was viewed as the death of one's spouse, and given a mean value of 100. All other events, in total 42, were rated in comparison with this event. The results are shown in the rating scale of life events below.

EXERCISE: ASSESSING LIFE EVENTS AND THEIR IMPACT

OBJECTIVE   The purpose of this exercise is to give you an objective assessment of the level of change in your life. Although the impact of life events is affected by your disposition (see Step One), it has proved helpful to review the impact of different forms of psychological pressure, independent of the person. This allows a level of objectivity to be gained.

PROCEDURE   Study the table of life events and ring the mean value of those you have experienced in the last year. Once you have marked them off go back and total up the values of each of the events you have experienced. You may want to repeat the exercise for the previous year if this seems appropriate.

Rank life event	Mean value
1 Death of spouse	100
2 Divorce	73
3 Marital separation	65
4 Jail term	63
5 Death of close family member	63
6 Personal injury or illness	53
7 Marriage	50
8 Fired at work	47
9 Marital reconciliation	45
10 Retirement	45
11 Change in health of family member	44
12 Pregnancy	40
13 Sex difficulties	39
14 Gain of new family member	?39
15 Business readjustment	39

16	Change in financial state	38
17	Death of close friend	37
18	Change to different line of work	(36)
19	Change in number of arguments with spouse	35
20	Mortgage over £30,000*	(31)
21	Foreclosure of a mortgage or loan	30
22	Change in responsibilities at work	(29)
23	Son or daughter leaving home	29
24	Trouble with in-laws	29
25	Outstanding personal achievement	(28)
26	Wife begins or stops work	(26)
27	Begin or end school	26
28	Change in living condition	25
29	Revision of personal habits	24
30	Trouble with boss	23
31	Change in work hours or conditions	20
32	Change in residence	20
33	Change in school	20
34	Change in recreation	19
35	Change in church activities	19
36	Change in social activities	18
37	Mortage or loan less than £30,000	17
38	Change in sleeping habits	16
39	Change in number of family get-togethers	15
40	Change in eating habits	15
41	Vacation	(13)

42 Christmas   (12)

43 Minor violations of the law   11

*The figure for the mortgage has been adjusted from
£10,000 to £30,000 to make it a more realistic figure.

282 / 321

Interpreting your scores

Score of 100 or less: the amount of change you are currently facing
is not too high at present. You should not be under excessive
pressure from recent life event changes.

Score of 101 to 250: the higher up this range you are, the more
likely you are to be experiencing the effects of pressure. You have
had a fairly high degree of change in the last year if you achieved a
score of 250.

Score of 251 and over: you have obviously undergone some
major changes in your life in the last year. You may need to pay
particular attention, later in the book, to managing the effects of
change.

This approach to diagnosing stress factors demonstrates a number
of important points:

■ Situations at home seem to be more stressful than those at work.
■ Stress is the outcome of adding up all the life events you have
experienced recently; you may therefore be very stressed because
of several events in your life.
■ Pleasant situations can cause added pressure, hence the inclusion
of vacations and getting married, etc.
■ The ranking scale is American. Work conducted in the UK
showed two differences. The mortgage in the UK ranked lower
(managers have lower mortgages) and trouble with the in-laws
ranked higher (in-laws live closer).

The case of Martin and June demonstrates how one life event can
trigger a series of events. Martin worked for a large computer
company with a site in Scotland. They had two children, who were
at school, and June had just returned to work as a teacher, having

had a spell at home bringing up the children. Unexpectedly, Martin was told he must re-locate to the south-east of England. This meant June had to give up her job, the children had to change schools, and they had to move away from their families and friends.

In their case they managed the change successfully. They received financial help from the firm for the move. They had the emotional support from one another, and moved to an area where they were able to build up a circle of friends quickly.

REVIEW

To complete Step Four, review the changes you have faced in the last year, with the help of the questions listed below.

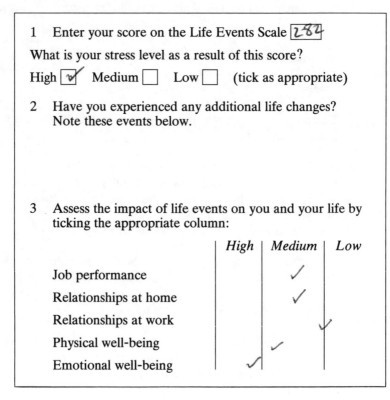

1   Enter your score on the Life Events Scale $\boxed{282}$

What is your stress level as a result of this score?

High $\boxed{✔}$ Medium $\square$ Low $\square$ (tick as appropriate)

2   Have you experienced any additional life changes? Note these events below.

3   Assess the impact of life events on you and your life by ticking the appropriate column:

	High	Medium	Low
Job performance		✓	
Relationships at home		✓	
Relationships at work			✓
Physical well-being		✓	
Emotional well-being	✓		

4   What are the most successful steps you have taken to adjust to the changes?

5   What were the least successful steps you have taken to adjust to the changes?

6   List items for which the adjustment process is still incomplete.

When you have completed Step Four move on to Step Five.

Step Five
Reactions to stress

Managers react to stress in different ways. Some respond positively with feelings of exhilaration and alertness – they are already thriving on stress. Others, especially those exposed to excessive pressure, react negatively to stress, by feeling irritable or becoming ill.

The purpose of Step Five is to help you to identify your reactions to stress. Once you can do this, and take action before the negative effects build up, you will have overcome a major obstruction to thriving on stress. Quick identification of your reactions is crucial for three reasons:

1   You need to establish whether you react positively or negatively.
2   The detrimental effects are less likely to build up, lessening the impact of stress.
3   Recovery from short periods of stress is faster. Recognizing reactions to stress can be difficult, as your response pattern is unique and may vary from one situation to another. You may, however, be able to identify typical responses, and to help you in this task you should complete the following exercise.

EXERCISE: IDENTIFYING REACTIONS TO STRESS

OBJECTIVE To help you identify the way you react to stress.

PROCEDURE Read each of the statements listed below. If the statement applies to you at present, or has applied to you in the previous twelve months, or at a time when you know you were experiencing intense pressure, then tick it. Be as honest as you can when you respond to each statement.

1 I am easily irritated. ☑

2 I have difficulty concentrating for any length of time. ☑

3 I feel tired even when I wake up in the morning. ☐

4 I seem to have boundless energy. ☐

5 I cannot take fairly trivial decisions. ☑

6 I have difficulty getting to sleep and/or I wake during the night and am very restless. ☑

7 I am achieving far more work than usual. ☑

8 I am losing my temper very frequently. ☐

9 I feel generally run-down and rather unwell. ☐

10 I am able to concentrate fully on what I am doing. ☐

11 Life seems to be quite hopeless. Nothing seems worthwhile and I feel really low. ☐

12 I have lost my appetite, or I seem to be eating more food to comfort myself. ☑

13 I have difficulty in absorbing new data. ☑

14 I suffer from frequent headaches. ☑

15 I am able to respond quickly to the demands placed upon me. ☑

16 I have difficulty recalling information when I am required to do so. ☑

17 I am drinking more alcohol than usual. ☑

18 I experience dramatic swings of mood – sometimes I feel quite elated, at other times I feel very depressed. ☑

19 I often feel exhilarated about what I am doing. ☐

20 I have missed, or been late for, one or two important appointments. ☐

21 I feel wound-up and am unable to relax properly. ☑

22 I am unable to achieve my normal level of creativity. ☑

23 I suffer from backache regularly. ☐

24 Ideas seem to flow more easily than usual. ☐

26 I have taken time off work. ☐

27 I suffer frequently from indigestion. ☑

28 I seem to lack the capacity to focus on a particular problem – my mind keeps wandering onto other issues. ☑

29 The least little thing sends me into a panic. I feel as if I am unable to cope any more. ☐

30 I have been smoking more cigarettes than usual. ☐

31 I have a frequent need to urinate. ☐

32 In discussion with other people I constantly repeat myself. ☐

33 My driving is rather erratic and my judgement impaired. ☑

34 I seem to worry about many things. ☐

35 I am mentally and/or physically very active. ☑

25?

Directions for scoring: identifying reactions to stress

Wherever you ticked a statement put a '1' in the appropriate box below. Each number corresponds with the numbered statement on the preceding pages. When you have done this, enter the totals of each of the columns in the boxes below.

1 [\ ]	2 [\ ]	3 [ ]	6 [\ ]	4 [ ]
8 [ ]	5 [\ ]	9 [ ]	12 [\ ]	7 [\ ]
11 [ ]	13 [\ ]	14 [\ ]	17 [\ ]	10 [ ]
18 [\ ]	16 [\ ]	21 [\ ]	20 [ ]	15 [\ ]
25 [ ]	22 [\ ]	23 [ ]	26 [ ]	19 [ ]
29 [ ]	28 [\ ]	27 [\ ]	30 [ ]	24 [ ]
34 [ ]	32 [ ]	31 [ ]	33 [\ ]	35 [\ ]
[2]	[6]	[3]	[4]	[3]

Profile of warning signs:

A	B	C	D	E
Emotional reactions	Disruption of thought processes	Physical illness	Behavioural indicators	Positive reactions

What does your profile mean?

A score of 0 to 2: if you have scored zero in each category there are a number of interpretations. You may have been dishonest with yourself, or you may be unaware of the signs you are manifesting. You may, however, be managing your stress levels very effectively already. A score of 2 in any category shows you have a tendency to react in a particular way to stressful situations.

A score of 3 to 5: if you have scored 3 or more in any one category this is likely to be a typical reaction. If you have scored 3 in more than one category this may mean that you respond in different ways to different situations. Alternatively, you may have been suffering from excessive stress for a long time. This is now manifesting itself in several ways.

A score of 6 to 7: A score of 7 is common for some people from time to time, so do not add to your stress by worrying – help is near at hand. Later steps will help you to manage your stress levels more effectively. First you need to understand the reactions a little more fully. If you have a high score for positive reactions, you may already be thriving on stress.

Understanding your profile

The reactions to stress most often mentioned by managers in the survey have been grouped into five categories for identification purposes:

A   emotional reactions (feelings)
B   disruption of thought processes (inability to think clearly)
C   physical illness (ill health)
D   behavioural signs (changes in behaviour)
E   positive reactions (signs of thriving on pressure)

These categories are not mutually exclusive; for example, you may become very anxious (an emotional reaction) and also develop a headache (a physical sign). Sometimes you realize your behaviour has changed, for example if you are unable to sleep. This change may be a result of illness or be related to emotional upheaval.

Beware of immediately diagnosing excessive stress because you are suffering from a particular symptom. Once you have read a book on stress a natural tendency is to assume you (and everyone else) are suffering from it. This may be true, but avoid jumping too quickly to conclusions. For example, if you suffer from a bad attack of indigestion there could be a physical reason which is unrelated to stress; on the other hand, your food may be too rich!

During prolonged periods of stress the categories can lead from one to another. When you are learning to identify the way you react to stress, you may find the process easier if you treat each category separately. A further explanation of each category is given below, to help you recognize your reactions.

A: EMOTIONAL REACTIONS

The way people respond emotionally to stress varies depending on personality make-up, early upbringing and life experiences. Some people remain relaxed and easy-going, even when exposed to excessive pressure, whereas others manage to build up even a trivial problem into a major disaster. Those who thrive on stress are likely to feel exhilarated.

Reaction to excessive pressure intensifies personality characteristics, making identification of emotional reactions easier as behaviour becomes more extreme. For example, the irritable person will explode at the least little thing, the inadequate person will collapse, and the anxious person will panic. Pause for a moment and think about your personality make-up. Which of your characteristics might become intensified in stressful situations?

As a child you probably experienced a wide range of feelings including, for example, anger or boredom. Gradually you developed particular feelings which you continue to re-experience in adult life. Parents influence the choice, discouraging anger, for example, but condoning helplessness. Consequently our emotional reactions are not always appropriate for a particular situation.

Bruce had been discouraged as a child from displaying anger and aggression. He had three younger sisters and he was taught to stifle aggression and anger. He substituted his anger with feelings of confusion, and under stressful circumstances this feeling dominated. If, for example, he was in conflict with colleagues, instead of an angry outburst which could be viewed as appropriate behaviour, he would become confused, an inappropriate reaction to the situation. Colleagues would often misinterpret this behaviour, making Bruce even more stressed.

Identifying your typical emotional reactions will need an awareness of how you feel in particular situations – for example feeling low or elated. Important emotional reactions which are stress-related include:

- irritability
- anger and aggression
- anxiety
- a feeling of hopelessness/depression
- swings of mood from elation to despondency
- withdrawal from people

Irritability

Most people will occasionally feel irritable. This is a natural reaction to the annoyances of life which we perpetually encounter. This reaction provides us with a useful barometer for measuring and recognizing excessive stress levels. If the least little thing annoys you, you could be experiencing excessive stress.

Mary worked as a teacher, and combined her career with bringing up a family. The job suited her circumstances well – her children were at school during term-time, and Mary was able to be at home during school holidays. However, during term-time Mary felt particularly over-loaded. As term progressed she realized she was becoming more and more irritable, particularly with her own family. At home she was always shouting at the children and complaining about their behaviour, and she felt unable to relax and enjoy life. Many working mothers will probably identify with Mary's experiences.

Anxiety

Anxiety tends to be a common reaction to stressful events and is probably the most important one. For many, anxiety is never far below the surface, particularly during times of change, giving rise to fear of the unknown and an anticipation of catastrophe. Even the most trivial events will be viewed as a source of stress.

A certain level of anxiety is quite normal. We all become anxious before a visit to the dentist, or a particularly important meeting or job interview. The over-anxious person will exaggerate every event out of all proportion.

James was always an anxious person, but when he heard he had been promoted to supermarket manager his anxiety level rose dramatically. He used to wake up in a sweat, terrified he might oversleep and be late opening the store for his staff. Would they all turn up on time for work, and what would he do if the deliveries were late were other worries which niggled him. By the time he reached work he felt a nervous wreck, and so each day continued. James was constantly thinking of the next possible disaster and became irritable and tired. Eventually, his area manager suggested the need for a reappraisal of his life. Only then did James realize the extent of his anxiety and the detrimental effect on his work performance.

Depression

If you experience prolonged feelings of pessimism, despair and despondency you could be suffering from depression. If you have had the occasional feeling of unhappiness when things have gone wrong don't conclude that you were suffering from depression. Identifying depression is a matter of degree – you inevitably have the occasional bout of 'the blues' but when this reaction occurs regularly you may be depressed. A common feeling associated with depression is inadequacy, resulting in loss of self-esteem.

Dennis described his job as a financial services manager, in a company undergoing excessive change. He talked in a dull, monotonous voice, complaining of his inability to cope with the demands upon him. 'Everyone else seems able to stay on top of the situation; I just seem unable to manage the change. On top of everything at work, I have been rather low at home, and now my wife is threatening divorce. There seems to be no future ahead of me.'

Dennis is fairly typical of the depressed person. Awareness of the problem is half the battle. You can then take steps to alleviate excessive pressure and become less emotional.

If you react emotionally to stress, which emotions are you most likely to experience? Once you have identified them you will greatly improve your ability to manage stress.

B: DISRUPTION OF THOUGHT PROCESSES

Another warning sign of excessive stress in managers is the inability to think clearly, or the disruption of thought processes. Specific examples ranged from a loss of concentration to indecision and loss of memory. These particular manifestations of stress have important implications for your overall effectiveness. The problem is exacerbated by a decrease in performance. This causes more stress, and traps you in a vicious circle.

Four thought processes are likely to be disrupted by stress:

- receiving information
- problem-solving and decision-making
- creativity
- retrieval of information

Receiving information

Throughout life you are constantly bombarded with a whole range of data, including facts, ideas, attitudes and beliefs. You receive this data mainly through your senses of sight and hearing. Some is within your range of awareness, other data is beyond it, and therefore never received.

At any one moment you only absorb a proportion of the information available. The amount you absorb depends on your attentiveness. This is influenced by motivation to listen, and your level of understanding of the information. If the information is unfamiliar, you can easily become overloaded and unable to absorb any of it. Stress also affects your receptiveness to data.

At an optimum stress level, you are far more able to concentrate and be receptive of new data. Once you react negatively to stress, your ability to concentrate drops and you are less aware of the outside world. In this situation you might describe yourself as forgetful; the problem is more likely to be a lack of attention.

Mark was a higher executive officer in the Civil Service. He was required to attend a range of meetings and produce the minutes. He was a conscientious individual and his superiors were always confident of his ability to report meetings accurately. Suddenly he started to make mistakes and miss out important information. No one could understand what had happened to Mark. In fact, he had been going through a divorce and was under severe stress as a result. The effect was a loss of concentration at work.

Problem-solving and decision-making

As a manager you need to be an effective problem-solver. To achieve this, you need to be able to think clearly, rationally and logically and focus your mind on the problem. When you are overstressed, all these processes become more difficult. You may have heard people say, 'I have so much on my mind I just cannot think straight.' Faced with excessive stress, a common reaction is to flit from one thing to another and achieve very little. You may experience difficulty with focusing the mind on one specific problem.

Faced with problems, and the need to take decisions, the overstressed manager is more likely to become incompetent. Effective decision-making requires time spent in concentrated thought. The over-stressed person always feels that time is a scarce commodity.

Creativity

Excessive stress also seems to stifle creativity. To be creative and generate new ideas you need to focus the mind, and let the ideas flow. If you are over-stressed, you probably have difficulty concentrating and getting in touch with the ideas. Sometimes the creative process can occur but you are unable to retrieve the ideas from the brain. Only when you relax do the ideas flow. As one manager said, 'I can spend hours at work trying to come up with a creative solution without success. I go home, have a meal, perhaps watch some TV, then relaxing in a bath the solution suddenly comes to me.'

Christine worked as a marketing executive. She had ten staff reporting to her, and her boss made heavy demands on her time. She felt continually under too much pressure and found her level of creativity impaired. Eventually, with careful time-management, she arranged two clear days at the end of each month, and always worked at home on these days to avoid interruption. She found that making this time available enhanced her creative ability.

Retrieval of information

Have you ever been about to introduce someone, and suddenly their name escapes you? This often happens when the circumstances are stressful, and you have reacted by mentally freezing up. This prevents you from being able to recall the person's name. If you know the people well you may react by saying, 'I'm sorry, your name is on the tip of my tongue.' More often you are left feeling extremely embarrassed, which of course further increases your stress level.

C: PHYSICAL ILLNESS

Medical experts generally agree that many illnesses are stress-related. Research has shown that chronic stress lowers resistance to illness and intensifies its impact. Even if your score for physical illness was zero do not skip this section. You need to be aware of the illnesses thought to be stress-related. Figure 7 summarizes those illnesses most frequently mentioned by experts as being stress-related.

Take a moment to reflect on your own health record. Have you experienced periods of ill-health? If you have been ill:

■ did the illness coincide with stressful periods of your life?
■ have you had recurring ailments and health problems over the years?
■ have you suffered different patterns of illness over your life span?

Some stress-related illnesses are killers, such as coronary diseases. Other physical effects are less severe. You may experience non-specific pain or just generally feel unwell. The impact of stress depends on the severity and duration of the pressure and your own vulnerability. Most people have one or two weak spots in their bodies. Prolonged stress can often lead to a particular physical response depending on your point of weakness.

Most managers interviewed during research for this book experienced a certain amount of stress-related illness. David, working in the publishing industry, was perpetually required to meet deadlines. He had recently married and was under considerable pressure at work. He seemed to survive during the week, but every weekend, when he relaxed, he complained of pains and indigestion. Friends joked about his wife's cooking. Eventually he consulted a doctor and an ulcer was diagnosed. Shortly afterwards he changed his job and his health problems cleared up. He has, incidentally, remained happily married!

Figure 7 Stress-related illness

Mouth:
  ulcers
Digestive tract:
  colic
  diarrhoea/constipation
  indigestion and heartburn
  ulcers
  diabetes
Reproductive organs:
  pre-menstrual tension (f)
  impotence (m)
  menstrual disorders (f)
Hair:
  alopecia
Bladder:
  irritability
  frequency of need to urinate
Skin:
  eczema
  psoriasis

Cardio-vascular system:
  heart attack
  palpitations
  hypertension (high blood pressure)
  angina
  migraine
  haemorrhoids
Lungs:
  asthma, coughs
  dizziness, fainting
  breathlessness/breathing difficulties
Skeletal – muscular system:
  muscular twitches
  gnashing of teeth
  backache, neckache
  tension headache
  arthritis

This last example demonstrated how symptoms of stress are not always apparent at the time of acute pressure. Only when you relax do the symptoms appear. Many people experience health problems, at weekends or on holiday, or shortly after the period of excessive pressure. Sometimes health problems resulting from stress occur as much as one year after the stressful event.

D: BEHAVIOURAL SIGNS

This category includes changes in behaviour which can be observed and recognized more easily, particularly by other people. If you are over-stressed your behaviour may suggest a desire to escape, for example avoiding contact with people. Your behaviour may reveal an attempt to console yourself, for example excessive eating or drinking. Typical behavioural problems include:

- poor sleeping habits
- excessive drinking
- excessive eating/loss of appetite
- missed appointments/lateness
- avoiding contact with people/time off work
- changed driving behaviour

Poor sleeping habits

Insomnia is a common sign of stress. You may be unable to relax and forget your problems, have difficulty getting to sleep and be disturbed by dreams or waking in the night.

Robin normally slept well until his new boss joined the organization he worked for. He gradually realized that as soon as he got into bed he started thinking about work. Robin was a systems analyst working for a local authority. In the past he had been given freedom to run his own projects but his new boss kept interfering. Robin became tired, irritable and tense. Finally he decided he would confront his boss. He managed to persuade him to delegate more and give him more freedom to manage his own work. Robin also resolved to relax more in the evenings, realizing that his boss might not change. Gradually the sleepless nights lessened and Robin felt much less tense.

Excessive drinking

Alcoholism is a growing problem facing organizations today. This may be a sign of increased stress. People who resort to drink are seeking refuge from their problems. Drink does nothing to solve the problem, it just makes it easier to bear.

Malcolm was a consultant with an advertising agency. He was required to entertain clients regularly and drank with them. His agency lost one or two valuable accounts, and colleagues blamed Malcolm. He found himself drinking more and more until in the end he could not face making a presentation to a client without having a drink first. Colleagues warned him of his excessive drinking but he seemed unable to stop himself. He became more and more incoherent, he lost his creativity and flair and ultimately the problem cost Malcolm his job.

Sadly Malcolm's case is a common one today. Alcohol dulls the brain, impairs work performance and damages the reputation of the organization. People suffering from alcoholism often find difficulty in recognizing and overcoming the problem.

Avoiding contact with people/time off work

People who prefer solitude and time on their own – sometimes described as introverts – are more likely to react to stress by avoiding people or staying off work. Over-stressed people usually feel fatigued, and introverts find the wear and tear of social contact too much to manage. Most jobs, especially in management, require a high level of contact with people which may over-tax the stressed person.

Driving behaviour

Driving is a skill which requires vigilant behaviour, judgement and tolerance of other road users. Many people, on becoming enclosed in their cars, take on a new personality, and a normally quiet person can become quite aggressive.

Sally, a sales representative, said her first warning of stress was a change in her style of driving. In particular, if a customer upset her she became preoccupied and more accident-prone as her judgement of distances was affected. She also found parking the car difficult.

E: POSITIVE REACTIONS TO STRESS

So far, the signs of stress have been negative, but the effects can be positive if you thrive on stress already. Focus on a time when you have been working under fairly intense pressure, and performing well. How were you feeling at that time?

In the survey conducted with the 200 managers, several described times when they responded to pressure in a positive way. Some of you will need and enjoy a fairly high level of pressure in your life. The managers interviewed talked of flowing with the pressure, feeling full of energy and enthusiasm and able to accomplish much greater volumes of work than usual. What they were describing were the effects of the physiological stress reaction. Their bodies were full of adrenalin which was making them much more alert and active. Apparently, actors need to feel a certain level of stress to perform well. When a study was made of actors who forgot their lines it was found that this nearly always happened when they felt too relaxed.

Responding to stress in a positive way therefore enables you to flow with the pressure, but like negative reactions, should not be allowed to continue for long periods of time. You are just as likely to become burnt out if you don't pace yourself correctly.

REVIEW

You are now aware that stress manifests itself in a range of ways. The early warning signs may be physical or emotional, and may be perceived as positive or negative. Ultimately the effects are likely to result in ill health if allowed to continue unchecked.

Recognizing you are suffering from excessive stress is one of the most important steps in managing stress. For this reason, spend a little time reflecting on the way you respond to stress. You may also like to collect the views of friends and colleagues to enable you to spot the warning signs, and manage the situation quickly.

To help you review Step Five before moving on to the next step, complete the summary table below.

EXERCISE: SUMMARY TABLE

Reaction	*Your personal reaction*
Emotional reaction	
Disruption of thought processes	
Physical illness	
Behavioural indicators	
Positive reactions	

Part II
Review and consolidation

Step Six
Review, consolidation and developing a vision of the future

You should now understand the factors contributing to stress, having completed the diagnostic phase. This next step will help you to review and consolidate your findings, and assess your current and desired stress level. You will then be ready to develop the most appropriate strategies and techniques to thrive on stress.

Thriving on stress successfully comes from clear answers to the following questions:

1   Where are you now?
2   Where do you want to be?
3   How do you get there?

By the time you complete Step Six you will have answered the first two questions. Question three requires you to work through Part Three of the workbook.

WHERE ARE YOU NOW?

To answer this question you need to have a clear picture of stress-related issues, your reactions, vulnerability and preferred stress level.

EXERCISE: THE 'WHERE ARE YOU NOW?' ANALYSIS

OBJECTIVE To provide you with a clear picture of the current situation.

PROCEDURE *Part 1* Reflect on your life at the moment, then give a brief description of:

- key issues in your life now

- your state of health and energy level

- any symptoms of stress

- your competence to meet current demands

- your current stress level

Part 2 Review the diagnostic steps, including Steps One to Five and answer the following questions:

1   Does your disposition make you more or less resistant to stress? (See Step One.)

Less resistant └__│__✗__│__│__│__│ More resistant
             5   4   3   2   1   0

2   How vulnerable are you to stress, in terms of lifestyle? (See Step Two.)

Very vulnerable └__✗__│__│__│__│__│ Invulnerable
             5   4   3   2   1   0

3   What are the major demands currently facing you? (See Step Three.)

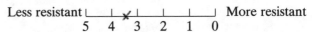

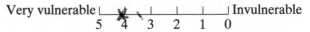

How would you assess these demands at present?

Very high └__✗__✗__│__│__│__│ Very low
         5   4   3   2   1   0

4   How much change have you needed to manage in the
     last twelve months? (See Step Four.)

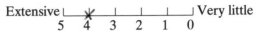

Extensive └──✗──┴───┴───┴───┘ Very little
             5   4   3   2   1   0

5   Would you describe your current stance on life as
     basically positive or negative?

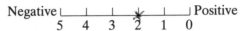

Negative └───┴───┴──✗──┴───┘ Positive
            5   4   3   2   1   0

6   How would you describe your stress level?

Too high └──✗──┴───┴───┴───┘ Too low
            5   4   3   2   1   0

Assessing current level of stress
You can assess your current stress level by combining the
scores and marking your score on the scale below.

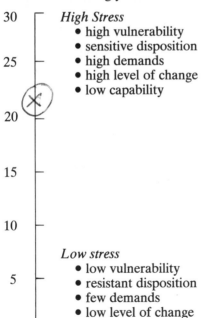

30 ┌   *High Stress*
   │   • high vulnerability
   │   • sensitive disposition
25 ├   • high demands
   │   • high level of change
   │   • low capability
20 ├

15 ├

10 ├

       Low stress
         • low vulnerability
5 ├   • resistant disposition
         • few demands
         • low level of change
0 └   • high capability

The scale above shows that:

- your stress level will be high when your vulnerability is high, you have a sensitive disposition, and demands and level of change are high;
- your stress level will be low when your vulnerability is low, you have a resistant disposition, and demands and level of change are low.

To complete this exercise, describe your current stress level by ticking one of the following:

1 Excessively high stress level causing distress.
2 High stress level on which you are thriving.
3 Moderate stress level on which you are thriving.
4 Moderate stress level which feels inappropriate.
5 Low stress level on which you are thriving.
6 Low stress level which is making you feel apathetic or frustrated.

WHERE DO YOU WANT TO BE?

To help choose appropriate strategies and techniques, you need to develop a vision of the future. Jerry, a production manager at a light engineering company, who had just come through a very stressful period of his life, said, 'I thought I would never feel the same again after a series of catastrophes. One day I was out walking and thought, why don't I try managing my life in the same way I manage my job. I went home and asked myself the question, what do I want from life? At the time I was feeling highly stressed, so I felt I wanted to be without stress. I wrote down a list of things which I would associate with a stress-free life. It looked something like this.' He jotted down a list of things, including some of those listed below.

1 Feeling full of energy.
2 Able to sleep well at night, and waking refreshed.
3 A sharp mind, able to concentrate well.
4 Enjoying a satisfying emotional relationship.
5 Able to like and enjoy people.
6 A successful career.

7 Optimistic about life and the future.

8 Taking plenty out of life and putting plenty back in.

To effect change in your life you need to have a vision of where you want to go. In the same way as you might manage a situation at work, you need objectives and a plan of how you are going to achieve them. You will also need criteria for success. All of these are achievable once you have developed a vision.

EXERCISE: DEVELOPING A VISION OF THE FUTURE

OBJECTIVE To develop a clear visual integrated picture, in sufficient focus, to provide the basis for action planning.

PROCEDURE To develop this vision you will need to choose a quiet time, when you have a couple of uninterrupted hours. Then complete the following steps:

1 Think back over at least the last ten years and write out a description of your life, with particular reference to stress. You will need a separate piece of paper for this exercise. If you are artistic you may like to draw a picture of your vision. Include in this step:

- key life events related to work and outside work

- your thoughts and feelings at the time

- your state of health and energy level

- any stress, and the symptoms

- how you attempted to cope with the stress

2 Read your description and ask yourself:

- are there any recurring themes?

- what causes me stress and what are the signs?

- is there anything I want to change?

- what would I like to be different?

- do I want to increase or reduce my stress level?

3   On a piece of paper, write a short description of your future life, again with particular reference to stress. Include in your description all those items you would like to change or be different. Include your preferred stress level.

Once you have completed Step Six you should have a clearer view of where you are and where you want to be. Section Three will help you to achieve your objectives by providing you with strategies for thriving on stress. Before moving on, complete the review to consolidate your findings in Step Six.

REVIEW

Give a brief summary of
where you are now.

Give a brief summary of
where you want to be. ·

Does your stress level
need to be:
- increased?
- reduced?
- kept the same?

Part III
Strategies and techniques for thriving on stress

Introduction

You are now ready to embark on the next part of the book. On completion you should have evolved your own techniques and strategies for thriving on stress. This is the most important and probably the most difficult part of the process. It is also highly personal and will need to link closely with your vision of the future, identified in the previous step. You will need to reflect on previous attempts at managing stress, and will need a high degree of commitment, in order to experiment with new ways of thriving on stress.

First you need to adopt a positive approach to stress. A certain amount of stress is inevitable and beneficial, particularly if you work in a situation which is constantly changing. Your reaction to stress provides you with the extra energy needed to respond to change. Without that extra energy you would find the change process far more difficult. You may still be viewing stress negatively. If you are the conscientious type, you may have a fear of stress, and go to great lengths to avoid it. By looking at stress in this way you are allowing fear to stunt your growth. The anxious type also mishandles stress, by directing pressure inward, and becoming self-destructive.

Second, you need to manage stress levels. Some people seem able to withstand periods of intense stress as their lives undergo rapid change. This may be followed by less hectic activity, to allow time for recovery. People who structure their lives in this way are more able to thrive on stress. Others, such as the ambitious and lively types, lead highly pressurized lives, moving from one demanding situation to another, and never allow themselves time for relaxation. They may not realize the ultimate price they may have to pay, that of burn-out. It is far better to learn how to thrive on stress.

Lessons on how to thrive on stress can be learnt by studying the way sportsmen and women and musicians handle stress. They have to operate at peak performance at certain times and need to manage the balance between stress and relaxation. Those who are highly successful have learnt to enhance their performance, by taking full control of their situation. The level of pressure is neither too great nor too low.

Once you experience excessive stress there are a number of management strategies you can adopt to cope with the situation. Some of these strategies are successful, depending on your personality characteristics and the situation in which you find yourself. Others are less successful, and failure to manage the situation will further increase your stress level. You need to be able to identify less effective coping mechanisms, so that you can avoid these in future.

There are several broad strategies for managing stress. You can actually prevent stress from occurring in the first place; this is advisable if the effects of stress are likely to be harmful. Once you are suffering from the effects of excessive stress you can develop techniques which lessen the impact of stress. Sometimes situations are beyond your control, and little can be done to change the circumstances causing stress. A change of attitude may help to manage stress in these situations.

I believe there is no one management strategy which will achieve universal success. You can thrive on stress if you:

1   achieve the right balance between demands and your capability to meet these demands;
2   view stress positively and direct energy outward;
3   are aware of the alternative strategies for managing stress;
4   avoid using ineffective coping mechanisms;
5   select methods for thriving on stress which best match your personality and situation.

Part III of the book has been divided into four steps. *Step Seven: Assessing your current strategies* will enable you to identify how you currently manage stress, and to recognize ineffective coping mechanisms. *Step Eight: Optimizing performance* will focus on the relationship between pressure, stress and performance. You will be helped to optimize performance by reducing or increasing stress levels. *Step Nine: Strategies for thriving on stress* will enable you to review a range of strategies for thriving on stress. *Step Ten: Developing your personal strategy* will help you to develop your own action plan.

On completion of this part of the workbook you will be ready to move to Part Four, which will enable you to help others thrive on stress.

Step Seven
Assessing your current strategies

You may have already developed ways of dealing with stress. However, many of the managers I interviewed realized they often chose the wrong coping mechanism to manage their stress levels, which exacerbated the problem. At times of high pressure their main concern was survival, and their reaction to the situation was inappropriate.

Step Seven will help you to recognize the strategies you currently use, and identify those generally found to be ineffective for thriving on stress. Recognition is half the battle. Once you know the ineffective strategies, you can learn to adopt more successful strategies and techniques described in Step Nine.

EXERCISE: ASSESSING YOUR CURRENT STRATEGIES

OBJECTIVE To assess both effective and ineffective strategies you currently use for dealing with stress.

PROCEDURE Think back over the last two or three years and focus on the stressful times. Make a list of what you did to cope in the space below. At this stage don't worry about success or failure, you will evaluate the coping mechanisms later.

When you have completed the exercise below, read the description which follows.

Faced with excessive stress you can adopt one of four broad strategies:

■ ignore it
■ flee from it
■ fight it
■ manage it

On a short-term basis all of these alternatives are possible, and will protect you from the harmful effects of stress. In the long term, the first three strategies are ways of avoiding the core problems. Effective strategies help you confront the relevant problem and solve it. Step Nine will help you to develop management strategies which are more likely to have long-term benefit. First you need to be able to recognize the ineffective methods. The seven strategies described below are those which are most often mentioned by managers.

INEFFECTIVE STRATEGIES

1: Escape from the stressful situation (withdrawal)

One way of coping with stress is to retreat. As one manager said, 'I literally feel as if I want to go away and hide from the situation.' Withdrawal was mentioned when symptoms of stress were discussed. Absenteeism from work is a common sign that a person is under stress. This provides you with the opportunity to be away from the workplace, a useful strategy if you are suffering from overload. When you return the problems which caused the stress in the first place are still likely to exist, which makes it a less successful strategy.

A positive approach, if you feel you have the need to be alone from time to time, is to plan a day a month working at home. Alternatively, if you are unable to work at home, find an activity which enables you to withdraw from your normal day-to-day contact with people. You need to have time each month when you can step back from the demands made upon you by others.

2: Deny that stress exists (denial)

Denial is a difficult strategy to recognize in yourself, and much easier to observe in the behaviour of others. Some of the managers spoke of colleagues who refused to acknowledge they were suffering from stress. One described the attitude of his boss, who said, 'To admit to suffering from stress is a weakness, an inability to cope with the situation.' Those who deny the existence of stress continue to drive themselves, rather than take steps to manage the situation.

You may have adopted this approach if you are an ambitious manager. When your performance starts to fall off as a result of excessive stress you are likely to work harder to compensate, repressing the signs of stress. Denying that stress exists is likely to exacerbate the problem and has been shown by research workers to be correlated with stress-related illnesses. If this is a strategy you currently use, be prepared to admit to it and take positive steps to improve your situation.

3: See your problem as other people's problems (projection)

The projection technique means you attribute your problems to others. Using this strategy you may say to yourself, 'Other people around me – colleagues or spouse – are suffering from stress, but not me.' If you have ever been on the receiving end of this strategy you will know that it is a powerful technique. Those around you may actually believe they are suffering from stress. This approach creates misery for others and doesn't improve your situation. Obviously, you need to accept that you are suffering from stress and start to manage it more effectively.

4: Become obsessional about achieving routine work

If you find part of your job stressful you may channel your energies into routine or unimportant tasks to help block out or avoid the cause of your stress. If you adopt this approach you may indulge in ritual behaviour or do routine work. You may start to do work that could easily be done by a secretary or a subordinate. To avoid falling into this trap you should assess what you have achieved each week. Ask yourself if you have been doing tasks which could be more appropriately completed by others.

5: Work harder

So far the strategies described have been attempts to avoid or escape from stress. A great temptation, particularly if you are an ambitious type, is to work harder when you are suffering from stress. This is an attempt to fight stress, and is likely to result in exhaustion. Once you suffer from stress you work less effectively and, in your desire to achieve, are often tempted to work longer hours to complete your job. This is not the way to achieve effective performance. You just become swept up in a spiral of taking longer and longer to achieve less and less. To break the spiral, be firm and give yourself time to assess your situation and do those things which help you to achieve your goals.

6: Become over-emotional

Several managers referred to outbursts of temper, excessive worry or feeling upset as a reaction to stress, and to allowing themselves to remain in this emotional state. In this state you may feel you are on a knife-edge, or in crisis, and you are likely to transmit this tension to others. Faced with this reaction you need to adopt a strategy which will help lower your stress level. Rest and relaxation, and addressing the cause of the problem, are the steps most likely to help.

7: Resort to props

Regrettably some managers still try to escape from the problem by taking tranquilizers, or drinking and smoking heavily. Whilst there may be short-term relief, the problem causing the stress is likely to remain. Once more, a strategy is needed which will help you to take positive action.

REVIEW

You are now familiar with common ineffective coping strategies. To complete Step Seven, answer the questions below. Refer back to the exercise at the start of Step Seven if necessary.

---

1   Make a list of ineffective coping mechanisms you have used in the past.

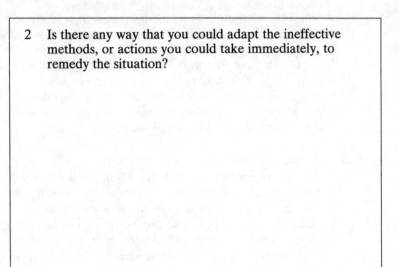

When you have completed Step Seven, turn to Step Eight to find ways of optimizing performance.

Step Eight
Optimizing stress levels to maximize performance

To thrive on stress you must optimize the situation in which you find yourself. This means getting the best possible results, in a given set of circumstances. To help achieve this you need to be able to manage the balance between capabilities and demands.

Some of you may feel that in today's society you are often required to work, or live, in unbalanced situations. In other words, you may find that the demands placed upon you, either by others or self-imposed, are too great, or not demanding enough, to match your capabilities and resources. This is inevitable, and life would become rather dull without challenges to meet, and without the need to develop competencies.

The aim of Step Eight is to help you to work in ways which will maximize your performance, by rising to challenges, building self-confidence, developing commitment and maintaining a degree of control over your situation.

OPTIMIZING SITUATIONS TO MAXIMIZE PERFORMANCE

Some believe that the way to control pressure is to keep it to a minimum. If you opt for this strategy it will certainly help you to live a secure, non-threatening life. It will not, however, help you to rise to new challenges and manage changing situations.

You might like to explore three alternative ways of reacting to challenges, which have important implications for the performance you attain and the stress you experience. The alternatives were first proposed by Kriegal and Kriegal, researchers in America. Their approach has been adapted to help you to maximize performance, and thrive on stress.

The way you react to situations depends on two factors: (1) your perception of your competence level; and (2) your perception of the level of challenge in the situation. The relationship is best understood with the aid of a diagram (see below).

Figure 8 The relationship between performance, challenge and competence level

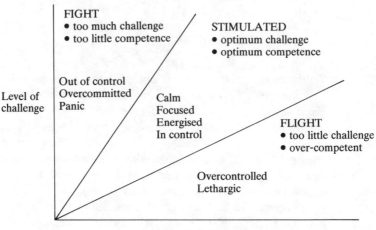

As you can see from Figure 8, there are three ways of reacting to situations, depending on the level of challenge and your competence in the situation. The first is the flight reaction, when the challenge is low, but your competence is high. The second, the fight reaction, occurs when there is too much challenge, but you lack competence. The third is the stimulated reaction, when there is optimum challenge and optimum competence. Your reactions are also related to your level of self-confidence; your degree of commitment; and your degree of control over the situation.

The three reactions, also called 'regions', are described in greater detail below, to help you to recognize your ways of reacting and to help you spend more time thriving on stress, thus maximizing work performance.

OPERATING WITH INSUFFICIENT PRESSURE: THE FLIGHT REGION

Those who operate in the flight region are drawn to mastery. They like to be very competent at their job, and never risk losing control. They like to operate in a safe region.

This way of working has important consequences. Instead of your job giving you new challenges, it becomes predictable, routine and dull, and you may lose interest in it. You are obviously capable of performing the job well, but without being under pressure you become apathetic, bored or frustrated and your performance is poor, unless you exert your own internal pressures and strive to achieve perfection.

Those likely to operate with insufficient pressure

Several personality types may gravitate towards the flight region:

- the anxious type – you fear uncertainty (this is secure)
- the calm type – you do not always seek challenge
- the nonassertive type – you may lack commitment and direction, and will avoid taking risks
- the conscientious type – you are likely to be over-controlled, partly through lack of confidence in your own abilities

What to do if you operate in the flight region

You must learn to take a few risks, stretch yourself, make a few mistakes and start to rise to challenges. Get the adrenalin flowing and don't keep too tight a control on yourself – allow yourself a little more freedom to experiment. If necessary, consider changing your job, or taking on extra or new responsibilities.

Lack of confidence may keep you in the flight region, and even when you take a few risks by trying something a little more difficult, you may not be fully committed to what you are doing. You don't believe you will succeed, the self-fulfilling prophecy prevails, and you fail. Adopt a more positive approach to situations and you are far more likely to succeed. Success will come when you learn how to operate in the stimulated region.

OPERATING WITH EXCESSIVE PRESSURE: THE FIGHT REGION

If you operate in the fight region you are drawn to challenging situations. You are likely to be very highly motivated to succeed, or like taking risks. You become over-committed, over-challenged and out of control. You are likely to want to do too much in too little time.

You are likely to drive yourself too hard and never have time to stand back and review your situation. Creativity is likely to be hampered, by operating in a frenzy. You need time for the creative ideas to flow. You may achieve less than someone who is not so over-committed.

Those likely to operate with excessive pressure

Two personality types are to be found in the fight region:

■ the ambitious type – you are likely to be driven by the need for achievement and become over-committed
■ the lively type – you are likely to be driven by the need for risk-taking and challenge; you may put yourself into situations which are beyond your capabilities.

You may find yourself operating in the fight region having been in the flight region. In an attempt to get out of your rut, you may change jobs. In your new situation you may lack the necessary competence and feel in a state of panic, and totally out of control.

What to do if you operate in the fight region

You need to learn to keep control of your eagerness. Learn to stand back, take time to plan and prepare, and channel your energy to achieving goals, rather than operating in an uncontrolled way. You will also learn how to achieve this by learning how to operate in the stimulated region.

OPERATING WITH OPTIMUM PRESSURE: THE STIMULATED REGION

Those who have described an experience operating in the stimulated region include a number of qualities:

■ transcendence – you achieve beyond your normal limits and are more effective than usual
■ effortlessness – your performance comes easily
■ positiveness – you are confident you will achieve and you feel good about what you are doing
■ spontaneity – your responses seem to flow naturally; you feel in good humour and your choices come easily.
■ being focused – you have absolute concentration
■ vitality – you feel full of energy and well-being

Balance in the stimulated region

Your successful performance results from a perfect balance between challenge and mastery. You set yourself just the right degree of challenge to match your capabilities and ability to handle the situation. Three other ingredients are also important and need to be in balance. *Confidence* – you believe you will achieve the task. Your belief is realistic, which helps you to undertake the necessary preparation. *Commitment* – you know what you want and go out to achieve it. You need to manage the balance between focusing on the future to give you energy and direction and paying attention to the present to maximize performance. *Control* – you focus attention and act on what you can control to maximize performance. You avoid focusing attention on factors beyond your control, which would lead to feelings of frustration and failure.

HOW TO SPEND MORE TIME OPERATING AT PEAK PERFORMANCE

The way to operate at peak performance is to ensure you have optimum confidence, control and commitment. Working on any of these factors will enhance the other two factors and help you to perform more effectively. Listed below are a number of suggestions for developing optimum confidence, control and commitment.

Developing optimum confidence

1   Identify the fears which typically hold you back. *Non-specific fear* – sometimes you may be fearful, but unaware of what you

are afraid. *Fear of failure* – this is the biggest fear which holds people back, but the fear itself is more a block to confidence, than making the odd mistake. *Fear of the size of the task* – when you are stressed any task or situation grows out of all proportion. When you are confident the task assumes normal proportions and becomes achievable.

2   Recognize the warning signs of fear. Tune in to the conversations you have with yourself. Your talk is likely to become negative and lack confidence when you are afraid. This causes you to panic or freeze. You also respond in a physical way. Look back at the physical warning signs of stress – these are the same when you are fearful.

3   Stop: take time to collect yourself and evaluate the situation rather than going head-long into it.

4   Assess the situation: you need to assess its difficulty and your own capability to manage the situation. This forces you to become more action orientated and enables you to take control of your situation and switches your attitude from negative to positive.

Developing optimum commitment

1   Assess how much you like what you are doing: make a list of how you spend your time and assess how much you enjoy doing the activities. You will never gain commitment to things you don't like doing. You may need to make certain changes to your life.

2   Try daydreaming to find out what you would really like to do: take time out to indulge in a little fantasy. Gradually, realistic ideas can be formulated. You can then set short-term goals to turn your dreams into reality.

3   Learn to achieve the right balance between dreams in the future and achieving current goals. You quickly become over-committed and panic if you focus too much on future dreams. Alternatively, lack of dreams and a focus on today means that you are likely to lose direction and become lost in day-to-day activity. The peak performer focuses on goals to maintain direction, and the present situation to maximize performance. By developing optimum commitment you will obtain pleasure from what you are doing, feel more in control and increase your self confidence.

Developing optimum control

1   Learn what you can control and what is beyond your control. You can control your own immediate situation and how you respond. If other people are involved, they are beyond your control; you can only influence their behaviour.

2   Give yourself directives on which you can act: the action needs to direct you towards achievement of goals and improved performance. Positive thinking is not enough to acquire control.

3   Focus on what you can do now: this increases your control over the situation and builds confidence.

4   Learn to anticipate situations rather than worry about what might happen. This enables you to prepare for the event, rather than do nothing and be in a negative frame of mind when the event occurs.

5   Maximize the situation when the unexpected happens: learn to take positive actions, rather than focusing on what has happened which is beyond your control.

6   Learn to handle anger: this feeling develops from focusing on situations outside your control. Anger dissipates when you concentrate on doing things within your control.

The above three factors reinforce one another. Developing commitment helps to increase self-confidence. Developing control also increases self-confidence and vice versa.

You probably now understand the relationship between pressure, performance and stress. A certain level of pressure which generates a certain amount of stress is necessary to achieve peak performance.

■ Operate with excessive pressure and you are likely to be too out of control to achieve peak performance. You are most likely to become burnt out by stress.

■ Operate with insufficient pressure and you are likely to lack the stimulation and challenge needed to achieve peak performance. Faced with failure or boredom you either adjust and operate erratically or turn your anger inward. In this case you suffer from the stress of frustration.

■ Operate with optimum pressure and you are likely to have the right stimulation and challenge needed for peak performance. You are likely to thrive on stress.

The aim of this step has been to help you to use the energy derived from stress in a more positive way. To gain maximum benefit you need to spend time reflecting on a situation where you are under-performing, and develop a plan of action to put the ideas into practice. The questions listed below may help with your planning. When you have completed the exercise proceed to Step Nine to help you develop further strategies to thrive on stress.

REVIEW EXERCISE: OPTIMIZING STRESS LEVELS

OBJECTIVE The aim of this exercise is to help you to operate at peak performance.

PROCEDURE Select a situation in which you are under-performing and answer the questions listed below.

1   Is your competence level:
     too high?
     optimum?
     too low?

2   Is the challenge:
     too high?
     optimum?
     too low?

3   How are you reacting:
     flight reaction?
     fight reaction?
     stimulated reaction?

4   To operate at peak performance I must ...

Step Nine
Strategies for thriving on stress

By now you should have a much clearer understanding of yourself and how you are influenced by stress. This step gives you an insight into the strategies available to thrive on stress. This is probably the most important element in the workbook. It certainly requires discipline and commitment from yourself. As I have emphasized throughout the workbook, stress is a complex issue and there is no one single winning approach. Probably at different times in your life different strategies will be appropriate.

In devising Step Nine, I have decided to adopt a holistic approach, one which will enable you to select approaches which will address body, mind and emotions. Each of these needs to be cared for if you are to thrive on stress.

Thriving on stress is difficult to achieve. The skills can be compared with mastering a foreign language. Initially you learn a few words and then can just about understand others. Speaking the language fluently requires diligent learning and extensive practice. Similarly, you can start to understand what stress is, how you react and what causes you stress. Managing stress so that you thrive requires considerable time, thought and practice to change your approach to life.

This step will help your planning to achieve a healthy balance between the mind, body and emotions. You will need to study the strategies, and then work through those which make sense. Once you have completed this you will be able to move to Step Ten and formulate your personal action plan. You may need to re-visit Steps Nine and Ten more than once to complete the process.

STRATEGIES FOR THRIVING ON STRESS

There are ten distinct strategies for thriving on stress. These are shown in Figure 9:

Figure 9 Strategies for thriving on stress

EMOTIONS
1. Releasing Emotions
2. Emotional Distance
3. Emotional Support
4. Emotional Control

PHYSICAL WELL-BEING
5. Diet, Rest, Exercise
6. Balanced Body
7. Relaxation

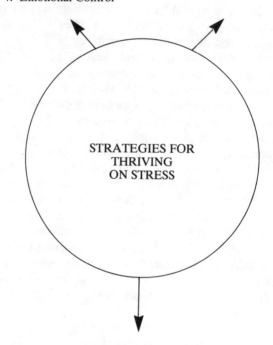

STRATEGIES FOR
THRIVING
ON STRESS

MIND, SPIRIT
8. Positive Stance
9. Realistic Expectations
10. Self Management

STRATEGIES ONE TO FOUR: SUSTAINING EMOTIONAL WELL-BEING

Many people react emotionally to stress. If this applies to you, you need to adopt a strategy which helps restore emotional well-being. Your emotions play a very important role in determining how you will react to stressful situations. Maintaining emotional well-being provides protection against excessive stress. There are four strategies for managing emotional well-being which will be useful from time to time. Between them they will help you to:

- release emotional pressure;
- rise above emotionally stressful situations;
- gather external emotional support;
- control your emotions to reduce the waste of emotional energy.

Strategy one: Releasing emotions

All counsellors know that people who do not fully express their feelings often become anxious, listless and troubled. I came across a tragic example of this recently. The parents of two teenage children were both killed in a plane crash. The daughter had a nervous breakdown but gradually recovered. Several years later she had grown into a happy, well-balanced person. Her brother tried to be manly and not express his emotions. Years later he still had psychological problems which were not resolved until he re-experienced the traumatic events around his parents' deaths.

Pent-up emotions do not disappear, but go underground and gnaw away at the individual's well-being. Venting the buried feelings surrounding very deep emotional pain probably needs the help of an experienced counsellor, but there is much you can do to help yourself. Find people you can trust who are willing to let you express yourself, and give you sufficient time. Say what is going on in your mind and allow yourself to react emotionally. Don't worry if you weep, laugh, feel frightened or distressed. Just allow yourself to let go.

Such expressive counselling can go both ways with people acting as facilitators to each other. The approach is sometimes known as co-counselling. It helps to release both deep and trivial tensions if repeated often enough. The principle is simple: allow yourself to express your deep feelings without inhibition.

UNDERTAKING STRATEGY ONE

Write a brief description of situations in your life which may
have left you with buried emotions:

Who can you trust and would be willing to help you express
how you truly feel?

Write down your plan ready for action:

Strategy two: Establishing emotional distance

Developed from the ancient philosophy of stoicism, this strategy
will help you to rise above the situation instead of reacting
emotionally and becoming a part of the problem. This strategy will
help you if you interact with others who are highly emotional. You
may find yourself taking on their emotional pressure unless you
adopt a degree of emotional distance.

During a lifetime you will experience many situations where you
will benefit from a stoical approach. You may experience excessive
pressure at work or be made redundant. Close relatives may suffer
from ill health or you may encounter domestic difficulties. All of
these events can cause undue stress unless you protect yourself.

The stoical attitude requires you to be less affected by the trials
and tribulations of ordinary life. This is done by building an inner

reservoir of peace within yourself. You have to condition your attitudes to expect periodic set-backs. You must begin to think of events as being like the weather – sometimes sunny, sometimes rainy – and realize that this is how things are, and will always be. Without rain you would not appreciate fine weather; without pain the sweetness of life would not be enjoyed. Difficulties are as natural as breathing. The developed adult does not allow himself or herself to lose their self-respect because their life happens to be in a period of disadvantage.

UNDERTAKING STRATEGY TWO

How have you reacted to past adversity?

How would your attitudes have to change to develop a more stoical attitude?

From   *To*

Do you want to be more stoical? If yes, where are you going to start?

Strategy three: Receiving emotional support

This strategy will help you to build up an emotional support network at home and at work. This will act like a suit of armour, helping you to withstand excessive negative stress. In ancient times people received such support from clans and tribes. We need to recreate such bonds and support systems. This strategy will be useful if you feel the lack of a support network at home or at work.

Belonging to a community provides a sense of meaning and identity which even has an impact on the proportion of people in the population who commit suicide. Many aspects of modern life are destructive to a community. You need to take initiatives to build up a network and support groups. This enables problems to be shared, difficulties to be put into perspective, and humour to be enjoyed.

Emotional support comes from having people around you who are positive and appreciative of your individuality and identity. Everyone has a need to be recognized and accepted for the person that they really are. True emotional support comes, therefore, from being both known and loved.

UNDERTAKING STRATEGY THREE

The areas of my life where I need support are ...

The people who give me support are ...

I most need support when ...

I give support to ...

I am effective at gaining support in these situations ...

My support network is ...

Too large ☐   About right ☐   Too small ☐

The quality of the support I receive is ...

I need to make the following changes to my support network:

Strategy four: Emotional control

This strategy will help you to gain control over your emotions. It is based on the assumption that thoughts precede feelings. If you can accept this assumption, you are then more able to prevent much of the emotional distress you cause yourself, by deliberately altering your thoughts. You alone have the choice, and are responsible for the feelings you experience. Thus you upset yourself as a result of other people's action, and you are not upset by other people.

This strategy is particularly helpful if you tend to react to stressful situations emotionally. It will help you to avoid spending time becoming emotional instead of completing the task in hand. This strategy will also be useful in situations where you have concerns and fears about future situations. You will be helped to develop a positive vision of the future.

UNDERTAKING STRATEGY FOUR

Make a list of factors about yourself which make you susceptible to emotional stress; are there any themes?

Make a list of things which trigger off your emotional responses:

Describe one situation in as much detail as you can:

What specific emotions did you experience?

What thoughts preceded these emotions?

What alternative thoughts could you have had?

How did you react to the situation and what were the consequences?

How could you have reacted more positively? Build up a vision of yourself: what would you be thinking, feeling and doing?

What messages could you give yourself to avoid mismanagement when an emotional situation occurs? (Possible examples: keep calm, think before you act, be positive.)

STRATEGIES FIVE TO SEVEN: SUSTAINING PHYSICAL WELL-BEING

The next group of strategies are designed to make you physically able to thrive on stress. Physical well-being interacts very closely with emotional well-being; a healthy body lifts you emotionally and helps you to approach life more positively.

The strategies will help you to:

■ follow a sensible diet;
■ develop an exercise programme to increase stamina and fitness;
■ take enough rest and relaxation;
■ keep your body chemically better balanced;
■ develop a programme for deep relaxation.

Strategy five: An effective diet, exercise and rest plan

This strategy will help you to thrive on stress by giving you increased energy to meet the demands placed upon you. Once you have developed an effective plan it should become a way of life – fitness has to be maintained on a regular basis.

This strategy is particularly helpful if you have a busy lifestyle and in the past you have neglected your physical well-being. By becoming physically fit your body will be able to counteract the demands placed upon it. You will be helped to plan your diet, develop an exercise programme and have planned time for rest and relaxation.

Before creating the plans, read the tips listed below:

Diet
■ eat regular meals, avoid too many snacks
■ eat as much fresh food including fruit, vegetables, fish and white meat
■ restrict your intake of sugar, carbohydrate, red meat and added salt
■ supplement your diet with vitamins, especially B complex if you are overstressed

Exercise
■ exercise regularly, at least three times a week
■ avoid violent exercise when you are unfit
■ do exercise within your capability range
■ select exercise you enjoy
■ try to include some aerobic exercise such as running, cycling, skipping, squash or an aerobics class
■ yoga and workouts in the gym will improve strength and flexibility

Rest
■ quality and quantity of sleep are important, cut down on sleep and you will need to work harder to achieve the same output
■ avoid stimulants such as caffeine for two hours before bedtime
■ get some fresh air each day to improve your sleep
■ take a catnap, when you can, to revitalize yourself

UNDERTAKING STRATEGY FIVE

I need to make the following changes to my diet:

To improve my fitness I will implement the following plan:

To ensure I have adequate rest I will:

Strategy six: A balanced body

In recent years we have learnt much from traditional Eastern therapies, including acupuncture, zone therapy, massage, and kinesiology to name a few. At first, Western medicine derided such practices, but some alternative medical practices have slowly become accepted. They impinge on the subtle electrical and chemical composition of the body to heal, nourish and revitalize.

When you are healthy all systems within your body receive a flow of energy. If you become overloaded with excessive stress some systems cease to receive energy, rather like a fuse blowing in a house. Applied Kinesiology enables practitioners to monitor the energy field by a system of muscle testing, and to find any imbalances in the body. Therapies used in Applied Kinesiology help to restore balance. The problem may be structural, chemical or emotional. The appropriate cause must be addressed to retain balance.

Like Kinesiology, Acupuncture is also used to re-establish balance. The flow of energy is balanced by the insertion of needles at specific points on the body.

Body massage can be used to ease muscular tension, dispel tiredness and to restore energy. The various movements used in massage help to relax tight and tense muscles. Massage also improves circulation and helps to encourage the elimination of toxic waste.

UNDERTAKING STRATEGY SIX

Do you feel ill at ease in yourself? If yes, what symptoms do
you have?

Have you, or your friends, explored any alternative
therapies? What were the results?

How could you learn more about alternative therapies?

How would you like to be feeling differently one year from
now?

Strategy seven: Relaxation

This strategy will help you to thrive on stress, by reducing your
level of tension, and lowering your level of stress. Once you have
mastered a relaxation technique, you will be able to use it as soon
as you find yourself becoming over-stressed.

This strategy will be particularly helpful if you are naturally a
tense or anxious person. It could be vital if you tend to lead a
highly stressed life. It will help you to restore a better balance in
your life by interspersing periods of activity with total relaxation.
Recently, for example, medical experts have expressed the view

that stress, rather than diet, is the root cause of heart attacks. The techniques include:

Progressive relaxation This is a straightforward approach, designed to reduce tension by helping you to control your breathing and relax your muscles. It will be explained in more detail later.

Yoga This relaxes the body, mind and emotions, and is the technique which is fully holistic. If you want to practise yoga you would be well advised to attend classes.

Relaxation tapes Several tapes are available to help you relax, build self-esteem and assist stress reduction. Alternatively you may find that listening to music relaxes you.

Baths, jacuzzis and whirlpools Very effective ways to relax at the end of the day particularly if you have muscular tension.

Engaging in an absorbing hobby or pastime Many people find total relaxation by spending time pursuing a favourite activity.

Using the technique of progressive relaxation
This is a straightforward approach to relaxation designed to reduce tension by helping you to control your breathing and relax your muscles.

1   Sit in a comfortable position with both feet on the ground. Alternatively, lie on a bed.
2   Close your eyes.
3   Become aware of your breathing. Count as you breathe in and out – breathe in one, two, three; breathe out one, two, three. Breathe easily and naturally. Continue this for a few minutes.
4   Become aware of your muscles; focus first on the muscles in your feet. Clench the muscles really hard and then relax them.
5   Relax all your muscles from toes to head in turn. Keep the muscles relaxed.
6   Continue breathing deeply for ten to twenty minutes. At the end of that time open your eyes. Get up after a few minutes.

Use the technique under the following conditions.

1   Practise the technique once or twice a day, but not until at least two hours after a meal. The digestion process seems to interfere with the relaxation response.

2   A quiet environment should be chosen, with as few distractions as possible.

3   Try to adopt a passive attitude. Don't worry about how well you are relaxing. To avoid distractions and maintain a passive attitude, keep repeating a word or visualize an object. This will stop your mind from wandering, which would prevent the relaxation response.

If you become really tense at work spend a few minutes breathing deeply. This will help to refresh you and lower your stress levels.

Meditation

Meditation is probably the most powerful technique for thriving on stress. This step can only introduce you to the technique, and hopefully stimulate your interest to read more or go to classes to develop your use of the technique further.

Meditation will help you to relax deeply. When you really relax the character of the electrical rhythms of the brain alters. Normally the brain's electrical activity is rapid and turbulent, but when relaxation occurs that frenzied activity gradually ceases and new rhythms pulse through the cortex. These relaxation rhythms, called alpha waves, have a deeply soothing effect and help to protect you against the negative effects of stress.

Recent research has suggested that meditation expands brain function by encouraging a balance between the left side and the right side of the brain, thus ensuring a balance between logic and creativity. To develop the technique of meditation

- Choose a time of day when you can regularly spend twenty minutes undisturbed.
- Choose a comfortable environment which enables you to relax undisturbed.
- Adopt a position either lying flat on the floor, sitting upright on a hardback chair or sitting cross legged on the floor. Choose a position which enables you to relax without falling asleep.
- Wait until you feel relaxed before you start to meditate.
- When you are ready to start, select one of the following techniques.

1 *Meditating by focusing on your breathing*

■ Concentrating on your breathing helps to block out thoughts. Close your eyes and begin to focus on the rhythm of your breathing.

■ Think 'in' as you breathe in through your nose, and 'out' as you breathe out through your nose or mouth.

■ You can start to count as you breathe, either repeating one or counting from one to ten. Allow yourself to become absorbed with your breathing and exclude all thoughts from your mind.

2 *Meditating by focusing on a word or phrase (a mantra)*

■ Occupy the mind by repeating your chosen word. You can choose any word, one possibility is to use the word 'relax'.

■ Simply repeat your mantra on each breath and gently reject any other thought.

■ If you persist you will feel an inner change in state which is the alpha waves pulsing through your brain and bringing a calm state of being.

■ You need to keep practising the technique to benefit from its effects. You will even be able to use it when you become excessively stressed at work.

UNDERTAKING STRATEGY SEVEN

Are there times in your life when you have insufficient relaxation?

Would you benefit from spending more time relaxing?

What method of relaxation would suit you best?

What do you need to do to implement the method you have selected?

How will you know if the technique has been successful?

STRATEGIES EIGHT TO TEN: SUSTAINING MENTAL AND SPIRITUAL WELL-BEING

The next group of strategies will address mental and spiritual well-being. To thrive on stress you need to be able to sustain inner strength. The strategies are likely to help you to:

■ adopt a positive stance to life;
■ achieve inner balance by adopting realistic expectations;
■ develop an organized approach to life.

Strategy eight: Adopting a positive stance

Some people adopt a negative stance to life. Such decisions are always taken earlier in life because the person felt that it was safer to be negative than positive. After all, if you are negative then you cannot be disappointed – you have opted out of the race and set your sights low. As an approach to life it is deeply unsatisfactory. What began as a protection mechanism results in a lifestyle which is a source of insidious and debilitating stress.

This strategy is particularly helpful if you tend to be negative.

You will be able to assess your current stance and will be given ways to become more positive if necessary. Positive attitudes are life-enhancing and become self-fulfilling, so leading to greater satisfaction.

Assessing the stance you take
You will achieve this by reflecting back over a period of time, assessing situations when you have reacted negatively, and identifying associated attitudes, thoughts and feelings.

Developing a more positive stance

1   Let go of the past if necessary: this technique will help you identify disappointments and failures. You may be thinking of previous jobs, relationships and dreams which never materialized. This was referred to in strategy one.

2   Adopt positive feelings and meanings: this technique will encourage you to find alternatives for situations you view negatively. You will gradually develop the habit of reacting positively.

3   Practise giving yourself positive messages: most people have an internal dialogue with themselves. You can either build yourself up or put yourself down. What messages do you give yourself? Put some positive messages on a card and keep reminding yourself of them when you feel under pressure. Do you lay traps for yourself? For example if you say to yourself, 'I haven't the skills to do this job' you are more likely to fail than if you say, 'I am going to rise to this challenge.' Once you have recognized the trap, you need to replace it with a positive alternative.

4   Develop a positive approach towards others: develop the technique of giving people positive recognition. This enhances their feeling of well-being and they are likely to reciprocate. Again this approach is habit-forming.

5   Enjoy the present: you have most control over the present so maximize the opportunities around you, whilst keeping an eye on the future to ensure sufficient direction towards future goals. By concentrating on the present you can achieve a better balance between activities and feelings.

6   Develop your independence: you have maximum control of
     yourself and very little control of other people. Whilst you
     have certain expectations of others, the more you are able to
     operate independently, the less you will experience the frust-
     rations of people failing to meet your expectations.

UNDERTAKING STRATEGY EIGHT

Assessing your current stance

List situations you view negatively, associated attitudes and
feelings, and positive alternatives

Situation	*Attitudes/feelings*	*Alternatives*

Developing a more positive stance

1   List events in the past you need to stop re-living:

2   List recent situations when you have been negative and
     identify more positive alternatives:

3   Identify traps you lay for yourself and substitute a
     positive message

Trap	*Positive message*

4   List ways you could give positive messages to others:

5   Reflect on yesterday and list times when you were living
     in the past, present and future:

6   How independent are you? In what ways could you
     become less reliant on others?

Strategy nine: Realistic expectations

To thrive on stress you need to adopt realistic expectations of
yourself, your job and the people around you. Needs and desires
are fundamental to the way your life evolves. At different stages in
life you need to re-evaluate your needs and set more realistic
expectations to enable you to thrive. Examples of people who have
set unrealistic expectations for themselves include the tone-deaf
music aspirant and the manager who expects to solve all his/her
problems.

This strategy will be useful if stress occurs as a result of a
mismatch between needs, expectations and reality. You may have
highlighted this as a source of stress in Step Three. The bigger the
mismatch, the greater the level of stress. Clearly a moderate
mismatch is likely to act as a motivator to reduce the gap. A larger
gap will result in frustration, resentment and misery.

To recap, important needs include:

- material rewards
- security
- power
- affiliation
- autonomy
- recognition
- status
- achievement
- meaningful work

You need to distinguish between basic, innate needs, such as the need for food, shelter and water which are physiological, and the psychological needs such as the need for recognition, affiliation and status. Psychological needs are unconsciously chosen by the person within a given social setting. You can learn to recognize your needs and adopt expectations which are realistic. For example, at one stage in my career there was no scope for promotion. I am highly ambitious, but realized at that stage that there was no scope to satisfy my need for advancement, so I channelled my energies into achieving high levels of performance.

If you reflect over your life you will realize that at different stages different needs are important. When you first start work material rewards are often important, as you are earning less. Affiliation needs may also be important. You may then have settled down and started a family, and affiliation needs are satisfied. At this stage achievement and advancement at work may start to assume importance.

You probably also realize that a satisfied need no longer motivates you. An unsatisfied need can grow out of all proportion and generate considerable stress. To experience inner balance you need to ensure your expectations are realistic. If they are unrealistic you must adjust your expectations so that they become achievable.

UNDERTAKING STRATEGY NINE

1   What needs do you seek to satisfy at present? Are any of these needs unrealistic?

2 How could you adjust your expectations so that they become achievable?

3 What would you need to do to meet your expectations?

Strategy ten: Self-management

If you study several people you will realize that individuals spend their time very differently. Some operate in a frenzy of activity, are always time-driven and never have any time to spare; others seem to do very little. The successful self-manager has learnt to create time for work and leisure: time for activity and for reflection. He or she has achieved a balance in his/her life and views time as money. This strategy will be useful for you if you lack peace of mind because you are disorganized, overloaded or lack direction. It will enable you to become more ordered and in control of your life.

One study showed that people were less likely to suffer from stress-related illnesses if they separated work and home life. Try to discipline yourself to leave work at the office. If you do bring work home do not allow it to encroach too much on your leisure time.

Effective self-management can be achieved by adhering to a number of rules:

■ Develop a clear overall plan by setting yourself objectives and sub-objectives in each of your key result areas.
■ Develop action plans which convert goals into action.
■ Establish a clear system of priorities: ensure that you include proactive as well as reactive tasks.
■ Use your time effectively by avoiding time-wasters such as interruptions, procrastination, lack of organization etc.
■ Delegate as much work as you can.

■ Identify the time of day when you work most effectively, and schedule difficult work at that time.

■ Regularly review your progress and make improvements to your self-management when necessary.

■ Develop a time management system which works for you.

■ Have an effective system for coping with paperwork.

■ Learn to say no when necessary.

If you have a serious problem managing yourself, attend a time management workshop to develop your skills.

UNDERTAKING STRATEGY TEN

List what helps you to manage yourself effectively:

What are your key blockages to effective self management?

What could you do to remove these blockages?

What else could you do to manage yourself more effectively?

If necessary, complete a time log and develop a further action plan.

REVIEW

To review Step Nine rank the strategies in order of their use to you and then proceed to Step Ten to develop your personal strategy.

Strategy		*Your ranking*
Strategy one	Releasing emotions	☐
Strategy two	Emotional distance	☐
Strategy three	Emotional support	☐
Strategy four	Emotional control	☐
Strategy five	Diet, rest, exercise	☐
Strategy six	Balanced body	☐
Strategy seven	Relaxation	☐
Strategy eight	Positive stance	☐
Strategy nine	Realistic expectations	☐
Strategy ten	Self-management	☐
Strategy eleven	Meditation	☐

Step Ten
Developing your personal strategy

The purpose of this step is to identify what you need to do, to implement your strategy and establish an action plan. By writing down the steps you will increase the likelihood of success. You would also benefit from sharing your action plan with a friend or colleague.

To help develop your plan of action, answer the following questions.

1   What is the specific issue/problem you are going to tackle? Try and be as specific as possible and don't be too ambitious.

2   Set yourself a clear, specific objective (for example, to improve your fitness level by taking more exercise).

3   Lay out a plan of what has to be done to achieve your objective.

4   To implement your plan what specific changes in behaviour will you need to make?

I will do more . . .

I will improve . . .

I will start to . . .

I will do less . . .

I will stop . . .

5   What do you do already which helps you handle your
     issue/problem?

6   What support do you need from others, and whose
     support do you need?

7   In the space below write some personal messages to help
     you when you experience difficulties.

8   How will you know if you have successfully
     implemented your strategy?

You are now ready to implement your plan. Take it a step at a
time and don't be discouraged if it takes longer to achieve the
results than you had anticipated. Good luck with managing the
balance.

Part IV
Helping others to thrive on stress

Step Eleven
Helping others to thrive on stress

So far the focus of the workbook has been on helping you to thrive on stress. To be an effective manager you need to be skilled at helping people to thrive around you, both at work and outside work. This step will enable you to do three things:

1   create optimum stress levels
2   prevent excessive stress in others
3   help others cope with excessive stress

Whilst this step is primarily aimed at the work situation, you will also find parts which will apply outside work.

First you need to assess the way you currently manage the stress of others. You can then read the rest of Step Eleven and compare the approach with your own, making the necessary changes if this is appropriate.

EXERCISE: HELPING OTHERS TO THRIVE ON STRESS

OBJECTIVE   To assess your current approach to managing the stress of others.

PROCEDURE   Complete this exercise by answering the questions listed below.

How do you currently ensure that the stress levels of others are at the optimum level?

What do you currently do, as a manager, to prevent excessive stress developing in others?

What do you currently do to prevent excessive stress developing in your personal relationships?

What do you currently do to help others cope with excessive stress?

CREATING OPTIMUM STRESS LEVELS

Step Eight outlined a method for optimizing performance. Much of what you learnt in that step can be applied to help others thrive on stress. First re-read Step Eight then work through the checklist below, applying it to each of your staff and to your manager in turn.

Checklist to help others achieve optimum stress levels

1   Does the person have the right amount of challenge?

2   Does the person have the appropriate amount of control?

3   How confident is the person?

4   Does the person have the right level of competence for the situation?

5   Does the person have the right level of commitment?

6   In which region does the person usually operate – fight, flight or stimulated region?

7   What action could you take to help the person to spend more time in the stimulated region?

PREVENTING EXCESSIVE STRESS IN OTHERS

From my experience of running stress workshops and more recently managing a team, I believe there are a number of positive steps you can take to help prevent excessive stress building up in others. This list is not intended to be exhaustive, but it should provide you with a good basis on which you can build. You may need to read further on these topics.

Appropriate leadership style

Effective managers value the importance of using the right leadership style for a particular person, and in a particular situation. Hearsey and Blanchard put forward this approach in their situational leadership theory. They emphasize the importance of knowing subordinates and their competence and willingness to perform. Once you have this information you are then able to select the appropriate style.

By choosing the right style you will give subordinates direction, adequate support and guidance when they need it, and will know when to step back and delegate. This will greatly reduce the tension generated in your staff when an inappropriate style is used. If you have doubts in this area read Blanchard's *Leadership* and *One Minute Manager* to develop your capability.

Effective team-building

If you build an effective team, this will go a long way both to prevent excessive stress, and to help those suffering from excessive stress. This will require you to:

- set clear objectives for the team;
- be aware of strengths and weaknesses of team members;
- develop an effective way of working together as a team;
- create an atmosphere of openness and trust.

Good working atmosphere

People are sensitive to atmosphere, and as a manager you can lead by example. Participants on stress workshops regularly refer to the problem of stress dumping. Stress can be very catching. By projecting calmness, and providing the opportunity for openness and support, much unnecessary stress can be avoided.

Relevant training

This can help to prevent stress in one of two ways, either by providing job-related training, or training specifically related to stress management. Job-related training will ensure staff are equipped to accomplish their jobs. Stress management training will help to develop skills and techniques needed to thrive on stress.

Giving and receiving feedback

People have a basic need for recognition; one way of satisfying this need is to give feedback. This should be given on a regular basis, not saved up for the annual appraisal, and should be positive as well as negative. We sometimes give criticism freely, but are slow to offer praise. You should develop a two-way process to encourage the sharing of information.

Building stress-free relationships

You need a positive interactive style. This requires you to maintain a high level of positive behaviour when interacting with others. By adopting this approach you are far more likely to keep stress and tension out of the relationship.

Examples of positive behaviour

- listening with interest
- confiding in others, and keeping their confidences
- compromising and negotiating

Examples of negative behaviour

- behaving aggressively
- complaining excessively
- ignoring others

Effective decision-making

Ineffective, or a lack of, decision-making is a problem regularly given as stress-inducing. You therefore need to develop a systematic approach to ensure effective decisions, and avoid procrastinating. You will need to:

- set clear objectives, having clarified the situation
- collect relevant information on which to base your decision
- review alternatives
- make the decision
- formulate and implement an action plan
- review the outcome

Realistic working practices

You need to ensure that jobs are designed appropriately, and work allocated fairly, to prevent unnecessary work overload. This needs to be checked regularly. You must also set realistic deadlines for staff. An assessment of time utilization would also be useful for you and your team.

HELPING OTHERS COPE WITH EXCESSIVE STRESS

Once people are experiencing excessive stress the best way to help is to give them time to talk either with yourself, or to an expert. Several companies, whose employees are particularly vulnerable, have now set up counselling services to counsel staff.

To help staff yourself you need to have good counselling skills. Skills are developed through practice, but you may find the following checklist helpful:

- clarify the objectives of the session
- encourage the other person to do most of the talking
- help the person to identify possible problems
- deal with each issue separately, helping the person to identify relevant information
- help the person to analyse the data and identify possible courses of action

EXERCISE: DEVELOPING A PLAN TO HELP OTHERS THRIVE ON STRESS

The people who most need my help now are:

To create optimum stress levels I need to:

To prevent excessive stress in others as a manager I need to:

To prevent excessive stress in personal relationships I need to:

To help others cope with excessive stress I need to: